> *"Mathematic....................................... by man to*
> *grant h.."*
>
> Le Courbusier
> (the French architect)

or in a more light-hearted vein from Samuel Butler :-

> *For he by geometric scale*
> *Could take the size of pots of ale;*
> *And wisely tell what hour o' th' day,*
> *The clock doth strike, by algebra.*

To many people mathematics is a dull and difficult subject and therefore one to be avoided at all costs. However once we ourselves master the fundamentals it is no longer dull and the difficulties get less with continued acquaintance. No longer should the mention of subjects such as complex algebra and calculus be a signal for an undignified retreat. It must be admitted however that at times the study of even elementary mathematics may be somewhat tedious but take heart, on the other hand it can also be highly interesting.

Here we treat the subject in such a way that it should appeal not only to those studying electronic engineering but also to many requiring an introduction into mathematics generally. Much in the book is designed to provide a sound basis for further study. Electronics technology may at present be undergoing unprecedented change but fortunately for us, basic mathematics is not. It certainly is a fact that the World is being driven electronically so to understand what is going on, we must have at least a little appreciation of the subject.

The main object of the book therefore is to help students and all other enthusiasts to break the ice. Even the more adventurous are catered for since a brief encounter with calculus is included, mainly to show its scope and how it functions. To some the earlier chapters may seem to be superfluous in this age of electronic calculators but it is essential that we are in a position to check the calculator's efforts for it is so easy to have pressed a wrong button.

A glance at the Contents page will show the range covered and there are also Appendices to keep us up to date with the SI System and to help with certain calculations.

In conclusion therefore it is evident that our aim is not so much to become experts in the many techniques of mathematics but at least to appreciate the usefulness and how basically the whole range of mathematics functions. Good luck !

F.A. Wilson

Contents

Chapter 1

THE SCOPE AND SPHERE OF MATHEMATICS

The subject we now take for granted (and sometimes fear) has not been in the world for ever but it did arrive many centuries ago. From its early birth when people began to get wise to the fact that there were more than three of anything, to the present day when advanced mathematics occupies the brains of the cleverest among us, much work has been done in its development and use. There is little doubt that mathematics has a very real and definite importance in modern living for without it practically none of our engineering projects could exist. Accordingly a mathematical training is essential for all who wish to follow an engineering or electronics profession. We look at the distant past first.

1.1 Numbers Through the Ages

It was many years ago that people first started to count, even by using their fingers and then the first of the sciences, mathematics began its development. Mathematics may be considered as the science of numbers and quantity and its wide scope is clearly indicated by the index of this book. The main constituents are arithmetic, algebra, geometry and trigonometry, progressions and calculus. There are also many offshoots.

The Greeks are credited with the earliest mathematical thinking. Many centuries ago they began to consider numbers and their association with quantity. They were also interested in the way in which numbers could be broken down into *factors*. These are the numbers which can be divided into the main number without leaving any remainder. For example, the factors of 10 are simply 1, 2, 5 and 10 whereas the factors of 12 are 1, 2, 3, 4, 6 and 12.

Prime numbers about which we still hear today were also first considered by the Greeks. A *prime* number is one which can be defined as a number only divisible by itself and unity e.g. 2, 3, 5, 7, 11, 13, 17, 19 are the first primes. They found that when any number is broken down into its factors, these can be

1

further broken down into their own factors until only prime factors are left. This means that every non-prime number can be rewritten as a string of primes multiplied together, for example 96 can be factorized as $2 \times 2 \times 2 \times 2 \times 2 \times 3$ and 95 more simply as 5×19. They considered therefore that the primes were the basis of all other numbers. The Greek mathematician, Euclid was able to show that there is an infinite number of primes. Later on in the 1700's a Prussian mathematician, Goldbach suggested that every even number above 2 can be expressed as the sum of two primes. This we now take for granted because all primes (except 2) must be odd numbers (evens are immediately divisible by 2) and we know that two odd numbers added together always create an even. Examples are: $28 = 17 + 11$; $30 = 17 + 13$; $32 = 13 + 19$.

The Greeks were not the only people interested in numbers however, other nations began to get busy around the same time. The Chinese had already developed their *magic squares* which had fascination for those interested in playing with numbers. As an example and using our present numbering system, the simplest square is :

```
4 9 2
3 5 7
8 1 6
```

and it will be seen that addition of the numbers along any side or diagonal is constant at 15. Larger squares have been found which also work on the same principle. Other quite complicated methods were also developed. One of particular interest used around the 15th century was the "window-shutter" lattice for multiplication. It may look complicated at first but it worked successfully. It is assumed that two single figures could be multiplied without help. A lattice (of which this is a small example) was then constructed as shown in Figure 1.1 for the multiplication of, say 46 by 34. These numbers appear at the top and to the right of the lattice (shown ringed). The results of each multiplication are placed in the appropriate box separated by the diagonal e.g. in the top left box of the complete figure is 12, the result of multiplying 4 by 3. The top right box therefore contains 18, obtained by multiplying 6 by 3. The result of the

2

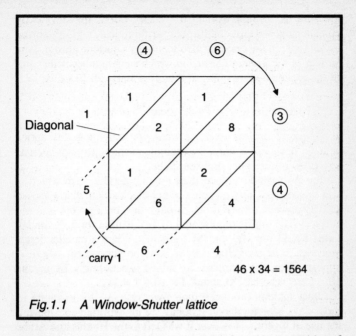

Fig.1.1   A 'Window-Shutter' lattice

complete multiplication is given on the left and bottom sides of the figure by adding diagonally as shown. Note the *carry* (the transfer of a figure to a column of higher value) of 1, this makes us realize that the method was not so far removed from present day simple multiplication.

It was the Chinese too who probably developed the oldest computing aid, the *abacus*. This consists of beads threaded on wires fixed in a wooden frame, it is still seen around even today but surely only for children, we ourselves have our electronic calculators. A simple abacus has 9 beads on each wire. Each bead on the top wire represents a unit while those on the second wire down represent 10's, the third wire for 100's and so on. Thus 56 would be indicated by 5 beads on the top wire, 6 on the second. To add to this number further beads are moved along the wires as in normal addition. As with the window-shutter method described above, a carry is also catered for.

Leonardo Fibonnaci (the Italian mathematician) developed greater uses for the abacus. In 1202 he published his "Book of

3

the Abacus" which expanded on the use of the device by considering various additional arithmetical and algebraic techniques. In the book he also mentions a curious puzzle, now known as a *Fibonnaci Series* in which each number is the sum of the two preceding ones. It therefore starts off like this:

$$1, \ 1, \ 2, \ 3, \ 5, \ 8, \ 13, \ 21, \ 34, \ 55 \ldots \ldots$$

a seemingly useless exercise until we learn that this series actually occurs in Nature, for example in spiral growths such as are found on fir cones and sea shells.

The Romans developed their own numeral system which is still in use especially on some of our clocks (note that 4 shown as IIII has been passed down through the centuries but it is not correct). The unit is represented by I, V is used for 5, X for 10, L for 50, C for 100 and M for 1000. When a smaller letter precedes a larger value one, it is to be subtracted, where it appears after, the numbers are added. Accordingly IX means $10 - 1 = 9$ whereas XI stands for $10 + 1 = 11$.

Other nations produced their own systems, for example in those days Mohammedan scholars led the world in considering the use of algebra. However it was left to the Hindus and Arabs to develop the system of numbers which is in almost universal use today and has replaced the rather clumsy Roman numerals. In fact the idea arrived in Europe around the 10th century but it took many years before it became popular. The Hindu-Arabic system we now use is known as a *place-value* method. This arises from the fact that the value represented by each numeral depends on its position or place within the complete number. Our system is based on a radix (root) of 10, there were others but they have now been superseded.

Before progressing further, let us be clear on what difference there is between *denary* (of 10) and *decimal* (of tenths or 10). Computers and the like have involved us in the *binary* system (of 2) so to be consistent it would appear that we should choose denary rather than decimal. However there is a difference which we should note. Denary numbers are our everyday whole numbers whereas decimal numbers may be whole numbers followed by a fraction with a separating decimal marker or *decimal point*. Hence 8062 is a denary number whereas

4

8062.73 is a decimal number. Decimal has a slightly greater scope, moreover it is more frequently used, hence generally it will be found that occasions arise when although it would be proper to use the term denary, decimal is used instead.

1.2 Numbers Now

Clearly no self-respecting electronics enthusiast is without an electronic calculator nearby, nevertheless we ought first to brush up our school arithmetic and also recall some of the terms used:

a *digit* is any numeral from 0 to 9. The *natural* numbers are 1, 2, 3 etc. and any one of these is a *whole number* provided that it has no fractional part, a *fraction* being a numerical quantity which is not a whole number. There are several types of fraction:

(i) a *vulgar* fraction is one which is expressed by a numerator and denominator e.g. ⅝ where 5 is the *numerator* (the number above the line) and 8 is the *denominator* (the number below).

(ii) a *proper* fraction is one which is less than unity (from Latin, *unus* = one) i.e. the denominator exceeds the numerator. An *improper* fraction is therefore one which is greater than unity.

(iii) a *decimal* fraction is one which has a denominator of a power of 10, but almost invariably expressed by figures to the right of the decimal point e.g. in 8.125, .125 is the decimal fraction.

An *integer* is simply a whole number but it may be positive or negative e.g. +79 or more simply 79 is a positive integer (the + sign is usually omitted). −79 is a negative integer (the − sign is never omitted).

Many manipulations can be carried out with numbers, below are some simple examples.

1.2.1 Addition and Subtraction

Here a *sum* is defined as the total amount resulting from addition, as an example the sum of 2675 and 5782 is 8457, calculated on paper by

$$\begin{array}{r} 2\ 6\ 7\ 5 \\ 5\ 7\ 8\ 2 \\ \hline 8\ 4\ 5\ 7 \end{array}$$

How do we do it? Firstly recall that when we move one place to the left, the numbers in that particular column have 10 times the value e.g. in the number 2675, the 5 represents units, the 7 is tens and the 6 is hundreds etc. Accordingly 2675 is made up of $(5 \times 1) + (7 \times 10) + (6 \times 100) + (2 \times 1000)$. In the addition therefore we firstly add the 5 and 2 (units) to get 7 in the answer. Next we add the 7 and 8 (tens) resulting in 15 (tens). This must result in a carry of 1 to the next higher column. The whole addition process is illustrated by :

$$\begin{array}{l} 2\ 6\ 7\ 5 \quad \} \\ 5\ 7\ 8\ 2 \quad \} \quad \text{numbers being added} \\ 1\ 1 \qquad\qquad \text{carry} \\ \hline 8\ 4\ 5\ 7 \qquad \text{result} \end{array}$$

If however we wish to calculate the sum of, for example 8245 and –362 (in other words to *subtract* 362 from 8245) then it may be set out as:

$$\begin{array}{r} 8245 \\ -\ 362 \\ \hline 7883 \end{array}$$

Note here that in the second column from the right, 6 has to be subtracted from 4. We manipulate this by 'borrowing' a 1 from the next column up in the top line, this becomes a 10 when moved down one place so instead of $4 - 6$ we have $14 - 6$.

1.2.2 Multiplication
We are taught to use the sign "×" to indicate multiplication, however computers generally use an asterisk, *. In setting down any simple multiplication, the first term is known as the

multiplicand and what it is multiplied by is known as the *multiplier*. The result is the product. Numbers may be either positive or negative, hence certain rules must be followed:

(i) when two positive numbers are multiplied together, the product is positive.
(ii) when either multiplicand or multiplier is negative, the product is negative.
(iii) when two negative numbers are multiplied together, the product is positive.
(iv) when any number is multiplied by zero (0), the result is 0.
Accordingly:

$$8 \times 5 = 40, \quad -8 \times 5 = -40, \quad 8 \times -5 = -40,$$

$$-8 \times -5 = 40, \quad 8 \times 0 = 0, \quad -8 \times 0 = 0$$

remembering that a term preceded by no sign is assumed to be positive. We might next refresh our memories on the now rather old-fashioned method of multiplication, this might be as follows:

Multiply 86 by 32:

	86	or		86
	× 32			32
	2580			172
	172			258
	2752			2752

the techniques are slightly different but of course the results are the same.

Here is an example based on the well-known Ohm's Law. We should at this stage appreciate that Appendices 1 to 3 are there to help with symbols and units.

Georg Simon Ohm was a German physicist who in the early 1800's made a study of electrical resistance and our unit of resistance, the *ohm* is named after him. He examined the way in which voltage, current and resistance were interrelated and from his work the units we now use have been chosen so that the voltage, V across a resistance can be calculated from:

$$V = I \times R$$

where V is the applied voltage in volts, I is the current in amperes and R is the value of the resistance in ohms. What therefore is the voltage across a resistance of 21 ohms when a current of 3 amperes flows through it?

$$V = I \times R = 3 \text{ amperes} \times 21 \text{ ohms} = 63 \text{ volts}.$$

Ohm's Law gives us a set of equations which are of fundamental importance in the management of electricity.

1.2.3 Division
Although the mathematical symbol for division is $\div$, we will frequently find that the solidus (oblique stroke, /) is used instead, hence

$$12 \div 3 \text{ may be written as } 12 / 3.$$

Here 12 is the *dividend*, 3 is the *divisor* and the answer is the quotient. The rules for positive and negative numbers are as follows:

(i)   when dividend and divisor are both positive, the quotient is positive.
(ii) when either dividend or divisor is negative, the quotient is negative.
(iii) when both dividend and divisor are negative, the quotient is positive.
(iv) when the dividend is 0, the result is 0 because nothing divided by any number must result in nothing.
(v)   when the divisor is 0, the result is infinitely large (we consider *infinity* more fully in Section 1.4). This is clear because the smaller the denominator of a fraction, the larger is the value of the fraction, i.e. when the denomina-

tor is very small, the value of the fraction is very large. In the limit when the denominator is so small that it approaches zero, the value of the fraction must be extremely great, in fact it is becoming infinitely large.

Without a calculator, division may be accomplished as follows:

Divide 133 by 7:

```
        19
7 )   133
        7
       63
       63
       ..
```
an easy one but next try dividing 6789 by 19

```
         357
19 )   6789
         57
        108
         95
        139
        133
          6
```
and here we have a result 357 with 6 left over, i.e. 357 6/19.

The fraction 6/19 would probably be expressed as a decimal, obtained by placing a decimal point after 357 and continuing the division. More on this in Chapter 2. Again using Ohm"s Law:

$$\text{If } R = V/I \quad \text{and if } V = 15 \text{ volts}$$

which causes a current of 3 amperes to flow, then

$$R = 15/3 = 5 \text{ ohms}.$$

Here is another easy one:
   A car travels 220 kilometres on a motorway in 2 hours. What is its average speed?

The answer is given by distance divided by time taken, i.e. 220 / 2 = 110 km /hour.

Here is an up-to-date problem involving both multiplication and division:

Digital data is transmitted over telephone lines and the speed of transmission depends on the electrical characteristics of the line itself. Speed of transmission is measured in *bits/second*.

How long will a computer take to transmit a book of 50 000 words, each of 6 characters on average, requiring 8 bits per character at a rate of 300 bits/second?

50 000 words $\rightarrow$ 300 000 characters $\rightarrow$ 2 400 000 bits

If transmission rate = 300 bits/second, total time required for transmission:

$$= \frac{2\ 400\ 000}{300} = 8\ 000 \text{ seconds} = 133 \text{ minutes.}$$

If transmission rate is updated to 64 000 bits/second, total time required for transmission :

$$= \frac{2\ 400\ 000}{64\ 000} = 37.5 \text{ seconds,}$$

showing how much more quickly things can be done with higher quality transmission lines.

1.2.4 Fractions

We have already met a simple fraction in the above Section and technically, as shown in Section 1.2, 15 / 3 is known as an improper fraction because its value is greater than 1. As a reminder, when the value is less than 1, a fraction is said to be proper. In this particular case 15 is exactly divisible by 3 but if on the other hand the value of a fraction cannot be represented by a whole number but only by a combination of an integer and a further fraction, then the fraction is known as a mixed number e.g. 27 / 5 leads to a *mixed number* of 5 2/5.

A fraction is unchanged in value if both numerator and denominator are multiplied by the same number. However it is

<u>not</u> permissible to add or subtract the same number to or from both numerator and denominator.

Division by a fraction: invert and multiply e.g.

$$\frac{5}{12} \div \frac{2}{3} \text{ becomes } \frac{5}{12} \times \frac{3}{2} = \frac{5 \times 3}{12 \times 2} = \frac{15}{24}$$

$$\text{or by cancelling, } \frac{5}{8}$$

1.2.5 Ratios

A ratio is a means of expressing the relationship between two quantities, it is determined by the number of times one contains the other, quoted either as an integer or as a fraction. In general therefore the ratio of a to b where a and b represent two unknown quantities is given by $a \div b$ or more generally by a / b. As an example, if an item costs £20 in one shop but £25 in another, then the second is more expensive than the first by a ratio of $25 / 20$, i.e. $5 : 4$. Equally the first is cheaper than the second by a ratio of $20 / 25$, i.e. $4 : 5$.

Ratios are frequently encountered in electronics e.g. a 2–winding coil or transformer has its "turns ratio". The two windings are called *primary* and *secondary* and if the number of turns on the primary winding is represented by N_p with the number on the secondary, N_s, then the ratio is given by either N_p / N_s or alternatively by N_s / N_p.

Electronic amplifiers usually provide a voltage gain from input to output. Call the two voltages, V_i and V_o. Then if, as is usually the case $V_o > V_i$ (for the sign >, see Appendix 1), the gain of the amplifier is given by the voltage ratio V_o / V_i. Hence if a signal input voltage (V_i) of 0.1 volts produces an output voltage (V_o) of 50 volts, then the voltage ratio of the amplifier is $50 / 0.1 = 500 : 1$, more usually expressed simply as 500.

1.2.6 Exponents

An *exponent* is a symbol which indicates what power of a factor is to be taken.

When a number is multiplied by itself it is said to be *squared* or raised to the power of 2, i.e. $a \times a = a^2$. The raised figure 2 is the exponent (or *index*).

Similarly:

$$a \times a \times a = a^3 \quad (a \text{ cubed})$$

$$a \times a \times a \times a = a^4 \ (a \text{ to the fourth power}), \text{ etc.}$$

When a quantity is raised to a negative power, this is equivalent to it forming the denominator of a fraction:

$$a^{-2} \text{ is the same as } \frac{1}{a^2} \text{ or } 1 \div a^2.$$

Exponents and the rules controlling them are considered in greater detail in Section 2.4.

After this we will find it more convenient to use exponents when discussing powers of 10 or 2, hence:

$$10^0 = 1 \qquad 10^1 = 10$$

$$10^2 = 100 \qquad 10^6 = 1 \text{ million, etc.}$$

also:

$$2^0 = 1 \qquad 2^1 = 2$$

$$2^2 = 4 \qquad 2^8 = 256, \text{ etc.}$$

1.3 Binary Notation

Our everyday system is generally known as *decimal* (of tenths or tens) or *denary* (of ten). "Decimal" is the term mostly in use. We are taught the system from our early days and it is ingrained within us. However in the late 1600's Gottfried von Leibniz (the German mathematician and scientist) discovered that all numbers can be expressed by different combinations of only two symbols. Hence we see that the binary (of 2) system did not arrive with computers — it was already here!

So far therefore everything we have discussed refers to the decimal notation (*notation* is the method used to represent

12

numbers and quantities by symbols). With the advent of computers and modern transmission systems, the *binary* notation came into its own and woe betide those of us who, having lived until now with denary only, try to ignore the advancing binary. The latter becomes of increasing importance as more equipment uses the system. Accordingly we now have to get to grips with binary numbers and binary arithmetic almost to the same extent that we have already done with denary which in fact confronted us as soon as schooling began. Happily denary and binary are both place-value systems. Such a system we recall, means that the value which each numeral or digit in a number represents depends solely on its position within the number.

The *radix* (from Latin = root) is the number of symbols required for a given numeration scale, i.e. denary has a radix of 10, binary has a radix of 2. For the binary system we borrow from the denary the figures 0 and 1, 0 represents zero and 1 represents the power of 2 according to its position within the binary number. Firstly here are the main rules of place-value systems:

(i)   the number of symbols required is equal to the radix.
(ii) a number consists of an integer and a fractional part separated by a point. If there is no fractional part, the point is omitted.
(iii) the numeral immediately to the left of the point (or if the point is omitted, at the right hand end of the integer) represents units.
(iv) each move to the left multiplies the place-value by the radix.
(v)   the *most significant digit* (of greatest importance) is the numeral on the left of the number, the *least significant digit* is on the right (see Fig. 1.2).

All these rules of course are well known from our experience with the decimal system but it is as well to bring them into focus because they can be applied equally to any other radix. Although history shows that some early nations used radices other than 10, it is the advent of the computer which has demonstrated the fact that alternative ones are not only

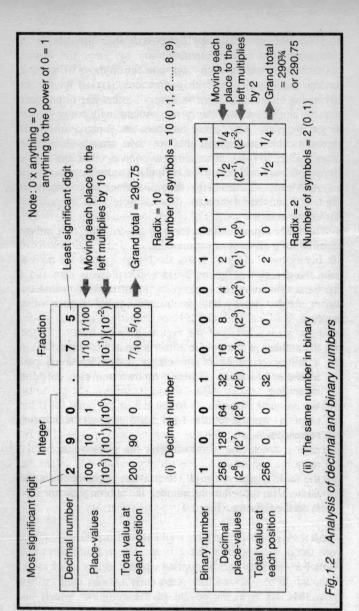

Note: 0 × anything = 0
anything to the power of 0 = 1

Most significant digit

Least significant digit

Moving each place to the left multiplies by 10

Grand total = 290.75

Radix = 10
Number of symbols = 10 (0, 1, 2 ..... 8, 9)

	Integer			Fraction		
Decimal number	2	9	0	.	7	5
Place-values	100 (10^2)	10 (10^1)	1 (10^0)		1/10 (10^{-1})	1/100 (10^{-2})
Total value at each position	200	90	0		$7/10$	$5/100$

(i) Decimal number

Moving each place to the left multiplies by 2

Grand total = $290\tfrac{3}{4}$ or 290.75

Radix = 2
Number of symbols = 2 (0, 1)

Binary number	1	0	0	1	0	0	0	1	0	.	1	1
Decimal place-values	256 (2^8)	128 (2^7)	64 (2^6)	32 (2^5)	16 (2^4)	8 (2^3)	4 (2^2)	2 (2^1)	1 (2^0)		1/2 (2^{-1})	1/4 (2^{-2})
Total value at each position	256	0	0	32	0	0	0	2	0		1/2	1/4

(ii) The same number in binary

Fig. 1.2   Analysis of decimal and binary numbers

14

workable but for certain applications, desirable (radices of 8 and 16 are also used in computing).

Figure 1.2 makes practical sense of the rules above using a decimal number 290.75. This is illustrated in (i) of the Figure and in (ii) is the equivalent in binary so that the differences become evident. Undoubtedly we humans will prefer to see things in decimal so equivalents appear as explanation in (ii) but we must remember that in binary there are no 2's, 3's, 4's etc.only 0's and 1's. The complete place-value system is illustrated in the Figure by showing a number containing a fractional part. Take heart, binary fractions are unlikely to worry us to any great extent!

Note that the 0's and 1's of binary may be referred to as *bits* which is a shortened form of *binary digit*. The two binary digits are sometimes described as *digital* 0 and *digital* 1.

1.3.1 Conversion of Binary to Decimal

The basic principle of conversion is not difficult to understand and Figure 1.2 has already given us an insight as to what is involved. If a binary number is lined up with its decimal place-values as shown in (ii) of the Figure, then for every 1 in the binary number the place-value is effective and for every 0 it is not. Totalling the effective numbers gives the decimal equivalent as shown. A similar example follows in which only the powers of 2 associated with a digital 1 are brought out to be totalled.

Computers work in blocks of 8 digits called *bytes* and the bit number as shown is the same as the appropriate power of 2 (the exponent), i.e. the most significant bit has a place-value of 2^7 and the least significant bit has a place value of 2^0. Here we find the decimal equivalent of 1100100 or as a computer byte, 01100100. The place-values for each 1 in the binary number are simply totalled, using Appendix 4 when necessary.

binary number...
(bit 7) 0   1   1   0   0   1   0   0 (bit 0)

decimal place-values...

2^7	2^6	2^5	2^4	2^3	2^2	2^1	2^0
	I	I			I		
	64	32			4...decimal total = 100.		

15

For quick conversion of any binary number up to 8 bits long to its decimal equivalent, Appendix 5 has been added.

1.3.2 Conversion of Decimal to Binary

There is of course more than one way of doing this, we choose one method which successively divides the decimal number by 2 and therefore avoids using powers of 2. It may not be obvious at first but the least significant digit of any binary number is a 1 if the decimal number is odd so if we continually divide by 2 to obtain the values of the bits running from least to most significant digits, odd decimal numbers leave a 1 in the appropriate bit position, even numbers leave a 0. This sounds rather complicated but it is easily clarified by an example so let us convert the decimal number 825 into binary. We continually divide by 2 and when the quotient is odd, subtract 1 from it and move that 1 over to the binary column:

			binary
	825	this is odd therefore $\rightarrow$	1
		.....least significant digit	
divide by 2	412	even	0
$\downarrow$	206	even	0
	103	odd	1
	51	odd	1
	25	odd	1
	12	even	0
	6	even	0
	3	odd	1
	1	odd	1
		.....most significant digit	

hence the binary equivalent of decimal 825 is 1100111001.

The principle used above is in effect that of moving the calculation one place at a time from the least to the most significant digit.

For quick conversion of any decimal number up to 255 into its binary equivalent, see Appendix 5.

1.3.3 Binary Arithmetic

On considering the four basic arithmetic processes (add, subtract, multiply and divide), we find that the equivalent binary processes are almost identical with those for decimal. Here then we do not illustrate each binary process with examples in this form but rather look at the way computers and other arithmetic processors do the job. It is a fact that from the addition process, subtraction, multiplication and division are easily derived. The processes may at first appear protracted but it must be borne in mind that digital processors can work at rates up to and exceeding one million operations each second! Firstly however let us refresh our memories on the process of addition, similar to that in Section 1.2.1 for decimal but now rearranged for binary. We choose two low numbers to avoid filling the page with 0's and 1's, say, 114 added to 183. Here is the general rule for binary addition:

$$0 + 0 = 0 \qquad 0 + 1 \text{ (or } 1 + 0) = 1$$

There is no 2 in binary hence $1 + 1 = 0$ with a carry of 1 to the next higher column.

2^8	2^7	2^6	2^5	2^4	2^3	2^2	2^1	2^0	value represented by a 1
	0	1	1	1	0	0	1	0	... decimal 114
	1	0	1	1	0	1	1	1	... decimal 183
1	1	1	1	0	1	1	0	0	...carry
1	0	0	1	0	1	0	0	1	...RESULT(decimal 297)

The process of addition continues up to the 2^7 column and we note that an extra column (2^8) is required to accommodate the carry from the 2^7 column.

Next it is necessary to understand what a *complement* does for it is especially useful in simplifying subtraction.

It can be shown that, given any binary number, its negative value is obtained simply by changing the 0's and 1's over. We can check this with any decimal number, say 93.

17

$$+ 93 \text{ in binary is} \quad 01011101$$

now change over the 0's and 1's to give

$$-93 \text{ in binary is} \quad 10100010$$

We are in difficulty however because we know that adding $+93$ and -93 together results in zero, yet above the addition gives all 1's. What is required for zero is clearly all 0's. The result above is known as the *one's complement* because it is complementary to an "all ones" figure. Somehow the two binary figures must be made to add up to zero. This is accomplished simply by adding a 1 after the change-over of 0's and 1's so that a *two's complement* is generated, i.e.

$$-93 \text{ in binary is now } 10100011.$$

Now adding $+93$ and -93 in binary results in all 0's, a true decimal 0. But note that the addition has resulted in a carry or *overflow* bit of 1. This raises an important point which is that, with binary subtraction by the above method of 2's complement addition, the carry or overflow bit must be rejected. Take a simple example: decimal 9 = binary 1001, the binary 2's complement is therefore $(0110 + 1) = 0111$. Hence:

$$\text{decimal } 9 - 9 = 0,$$

in binary $\qquad 1001 + 0111 = (1)0000$

thus the most significant bit of the binary is automatically rejected.

Accordingly, because the two's complement is easily generated, it is possible for a binary adder to be used for subtraction.

Let us sum the binary arithmetic processes up by considering two simple numbers only, say 12 and 3:

(i) subtracting 3 from 12 (= 9). But we could have *added* 12 and (−3). This is done by changing the 3 into its complement. Note that both numbers must consist of the same number of digits:

decimal 12 in binary is 1100,
3 in binary is 0011

(Appendix 5) and two's complement to produce -3 is

$$(1100 + 1) = 1101.$$

Adding:
$$
\begin{array}{r}
1\,1\,0\,0 \\
1\,1\,0\,1 \\
\hline
1\,1\,0\,0\,1
\end{array}
$$

rejecting the most significant bit gives 1001, i.e. decimal 9.

(ii) multiplying 12 by 3 is simply *adding* 12 to 12 to 12, i.e. three 12's added together,

(iii) dividing 12 by 3 is given by the number of times 3 can be subtracted from 12, i.e. $12 - 3 - 3 - 3 - 3$, hence 3 can be subtracted 4 times.

We will not here overburden ourselves with the alternative processes of binary subtraction, multiplication and division which are very similar to the decimal techniques. They can easily be explored and verified if required.

1.4 Infinity and Zero

From time immemorial mathematicians had been puzzled by the idea of infinity. They looked upon it as a kind of intangible number used for describing things which cannot be counted. The simplest example is the number series 1, 2, 3, 4, 5, etc., which has no final number for the obvious reason that whatever number we consider, it is still possible to add 1 and go even higher. This therefore is one of the mathematical concepts which no doubt frustrates many of us. We naturally are bemused on being told that parallel lines meet at infinity when in fact we know that they can never meet at all.

Infinite according to the dictionary means "having no limit or end, immeasurably great in extent" etc. We could ourselves add to this "immeasurably small" for we frequently talk of *infinitely* small increments. This now brings us into contact with *zero*, a better understood term. The link between infinity (symbol ∞) and zero may be demonstrated as follows.

The reciprocal of 0.1 is 10, of 0.001 is 1000 and of 0.000001 it is one million. Clearly as the number diminishes, its reciprocal increases so that at the limit when the number is actually zero, its reciprocal has become infinitely large,

Thus $$\frac{1}{0} = \infty \quad \text{hence} \quad \frac{1}{\infty} = 0.$$

Obviously infinity is more a theoretical than a practical concept and fortunately the difference made in a result by considering a large number or alternatively an infinitely large one is usually negligible.

As a practical example, theoretically a capacitor needs an infinite time to charge (or discharge) fully. Accordingly we have to adopt some convention to tell us when a capacitor is considered to be fully charged, this results in a length of time very much less than infinite yet quite satisfactory for most work.

Chapter 2

CALCULATIONS

The abacus was one of the earliest calculating aids and it has held sway for many hundreds of years. In the early 1600's however, John Napier made a significant advance in calculating techniques by his invention of the *logarithm* (from Greek, *logos* = reckoning, *arithmos* = number). This made the more difficult computations of multiplication and division much easier by turning them around into a form of addition and subtraction. Very soon after this, William Oughtred produced a working slide-rule based on the new principle of logarithms. This was followed by a great burst of activity in the development of calculating machines, the earliest even using gear wheels in place of beads on an abacus. Then in the 1800's Charles Babbage set about designing his automatic calculating machine, note the term *automatic*, indicating that the machine could carry out its task without constant attention as had always been required before. Babbage's work gave him recognition as the originator of modern computing. Unfortunately his main machines were never fully completed but it was recognized that the ideas they contained were workable. Shortly after this computing began to develop but we had to wait for the advent of the semiconductor to make high-speed computing possible.

Here however we must first ensure that we are conversant with the use of decimals before discussing the more complex calculation methods. Some of the more important features of arithmetic therefore follow.

2.1 Decimal Fractions

As already indicated in Sect. 1.2, a decimal fraction is normally expressed by figures to the right of the decimal point thus in 8.125, the decimal fraction is 0.125, the 1 indicating the number of tenths of a unit, the 2 indicating hundredths and the 5, thousandths, i.e.

$$0.125 = \frac{1}{10} + \frac{2}{100} + \frac{5}{1000} = \frac{100 + 20 + 5}{1000} = \frac{125}{1000}$$

or by cancelling,

$$\frac{1}{8}$$

so we can express 8.125 in ordinary fraction form as 8⅛.

If it is required to make the change the other way round, i.e. to change an ordinary fraction into a decimal fraction, then we simply divide the numerator by the denominator. Take first the fraction 3/10. This is easy because it is simply a case of dividing *both* numerator and denominator by 10, resulting in 0.3. Next try 18/25. Here it is possible to multiply both numerator and denominator by 4, giving 72/100. Next, dividing by 100, results in 0.72.

Where cancelling seems not to be possible, then long division must be used to divide the numerator by the denominator. Remember that we can insert as many 0's as we wish after the last figure on the right of the decimal point, e.g. to change the fraction 13/25 into a decimal fraction, the calculation may be set out as:

$$25 \overline{)\ 13}$$

but clearly no progress can be made so a decimal point and some 0's are added after the 13. Accordingly we have:

$$25 \overline{)\ 13.00}^{\ 0.}$$

and note that a decimal point has been put in the answer space above the horizontal line. Now the division can proceed:

$$
\begin{array}{r}
0.52 \\
25 \overline{)\ 13.00} \\
\underline{125} \\
50 \\
\underline{50} \\
\ldots
\end{array}
$$

2.1.1 Correcting to a Specified Number of Places

It will be found as we progress that some decimal fractions seem to go on for ever. A good example of this is the value of π, the ratio of the circumference to the diameter of a circle. This is equal to 3.141 592 654... and to be exact we should say "approximately equal to" because these figures are only the first part of the story, however they are more than is normally required. Accordingly there is a general rule for expressing a decimal number correct to a certain number of places:

> "the last digit to be quoted is unchanged if the next digit would have been a 4 or less but increased by 1 if the next digit is 5 or more".

Hence, correcting the value of π to 2 decimal places gives 3.14. There is no change in the 4 because it is followed by a 1. When correcting to 3 decimal places however, the 1 is increased to 2 because it is followed by a 5 so we get 3.142.

2.2 Percentages

Cent is derived from the Italian or Latin word for 100, hence per cent means per or out of 100, this figure therefore inevitably appearing whenever percentages are mentioned. We recognize a percentage by the symbol %.

Any fraction is converted into a percentage by multiplying it by 100 hence:

$$1/4 = 1/4 \times 100\% = 25\%$$

$$0.9 \text{ as a percentage} = 0.9 \times 100 = 90\%.$$

Conversely divide by 100 to reduce a percentage to its fraction, hence:

$$40\% = 40/100 = 2/5.$$

We could of course simply introduce and then shift a decimal point two places to the left to divide by 100, e.g.:

$$40\% = 40.0\% = 0.4.$$

In electronics many components have a *tolerance* rating. This is a measure of the degree to which the actual value of a component may deviate from the design or nominal value. For example a 1000 ohm + 20%, –10 % (tolerance) resistor may be of any value between 1000 + 20%, i.e. 1000 + 200 ohms (1200 ohms) and 1000 – 10%, i.e. 1000 – 100 ohms (900 ohms). This means that when we choose one of these so-called 1000 ohm resistors, its real value could be anywhere between 900 and 1200 ohms.

Percentages are commonly used with money, e.g. an interest rate of 9% per annum means that for every £100 invested, the interest added each year is £9.

2.3 Reciprocals
Properly defined, a reciprocal is an expression so related to another that their product is unity. In more simple terms a reciprocal of a number is 1 divided by that number, e.g. the reciprocal of 5 is $1/5 = 0.2$.

Negative exponents are also used to indicate reciprocals, e.g.

$$2^3 = 8 \text{ but } 2^{-3} = 1/8 = 0.125.$$

2.4 Exponents
Exponents are introduced in Section 1.2.6. In this Section we expand on their use and manipulation. We continue to use a, b, c, etc., to represent unknown quantities but any statement can easily be proved by substituting simple numbers instead. As an example, if as shown later, $a^2 \times a^3 = a^5$, then it is possible to substitute say, 3 for a to get $9 \times 27 = 243$, so proving the proposition. This of course is always a useful way of checking later that any other proposition is right.

The square root, cube root, fourth root, etc., of a number is that quantity which when multiplied by itself the appropriate number of times, produces the number. The square root of a is written $\sqrt{a}$ and $\sqrt{a} \times \sqrt{a} = a$. Similarly for the cube root of a, $\sqrt[3]{a} \times \sqrt[3]{a} \times \sqrt[3]{a} = a$, etc.

These roots however may be expressed by a fractional exponent instead of the root sign:

24

$$\sqrt{a} = a^{1/2}, \quad \sqrt[3]{a} = a^{1/3}, \quad \sqrt[14]{a} = a^{1/14}.$$

2.4.1 Negative Exponents

When a quantity is raised to a negative power, this is equivalent to making it form the denominator of a fraction:

$$a^{-2} \text{ is the same as } \frac{1}{a^2} \text{ or } 1 \div a^2$$

and similarly

$$a^2 \text{ is the same as } \frac{1}{a^{-2}} \text{ or } 1 \div a^{-2}$$

and change between division and multiplication can be made by changing the sign of the exponent, e.g.

$$\frac{b}{a^3} = ba^{-3}, \quad \text{i.e. } b \div a^3 \text{ is the same as } b \times a^{-3}$$

$$\frac{b}{a^{-3}} = ba^3, \quad \text{i.e. } b \div a^{-3} \text{ is the same as } b \times a^3$$

2.4.2 Multiplication and Division

(1) When powers of the same quantity are multiplied together, the exponents are added:

$$a^2 \times a^3 = (a \times a) \times (a \times a \times a) = a^{2+3} = a^5$$

$$a^{1/2} \times a^{1/2} = a^{1/2+1/2} = a^1 = a$$

(also proving that $\sqrt{a} \times \sqrt{a} = a$)

$$a^{1/2} \times a^{-1/2} = a^{1/2-1/2} = a^0 = 1$$

(and it is important to remember that all quantities raised to the power 0 are equal to 1).

(2)   When powers of the same quantity are divided, the exponent of the divisor (denominator) is subtracted from that of the dividend (numerator):

$$a^3 \div a^2 = \frac{a \times a \times a}{a \times a} = a^{3-2} = a^1 = a$$

$$a^2 \div a^3 = \frac{a \times a}{a \times a \times a} = a^{2-3} = a^{-1} = \frac{1}{a}$$

$$a^{1/2} \div a^{1/4} = a^{1/2 - 1/4} = a^{1/4} \quad (= {}^4\sqrt{a}\,).$$

Rule (2) is of course, rule 1 modified for negative exponents. As an example, $a^3 \div a^2$ is the same as $a^3 \times a^{-2}$. By rule 1,

$$a^3 \times a^{-2} = a^{3 + (-2)} = a.$$

(3) A product of two or more factors can be raised to a power by raising each factor to that power:

$$(a \times b \times c)^3 = a^3 \times b^3 \times c^3 \qquad \text{and generally:}$$

$$(abc)^m = a^m \times b^m \times c^m.$$

(4) A power of a power is obtained by multiplying the two exponents:

$$(a^2)^3 = (a \times a) \times (a \times a) \times (a \times a) = a^{2 \times 3} = a^6$$

$$(\sqrt{a})^4 = \sqrt{a} \times \sqrt{a} \times \sqrt{a} \times \sqrt{a} = a^2$$

or using fractional exponents:

$$(\sqrt{a})^4 = (a^{1/2})^4 = a^{1/2 \times 4} = a^2.$$

Powers and roots of fractions:

The exponent operates on both numerator and denominator:

$$\left(\frac{a}{b}\right)^2 = \frac{a^2}{b^2} \qquad \pi\left(\frac{d}{2}\right)^2 = \frac{\pi d^2}{4} \qquad \sqrt{\frac{a}{9}} = \frac{\sqrt{a}}{3}$$

or using fractional exponents:

$$\left(\frac{a}{9}\right)^{1/2} = \frac{a^{1/2}}{9^{1/2}} = \frac{a^{1/2}}{3}$$

Some examples will provide practical experience:

(i) $\ 10^3 \times 10^7 \div 10^2 = 10^{3+7-2} = 10^8$

(ii) $\ (1.8 \times 10^{-3}) \times (5 \times 10^5) = 1.8 \times 5 \times 10^{5-3}$
$$= 9 \times 10^2 = 900$$

(iii) $\ \dfrac{9 \times 10^{-5}}{3 \times 10^{-6}} = 3 \times 10^{-5+6} = 30$

(iv) $\ 2^{1/4} \times 2^{1/2} = 2^{3/4} = (\sqrt[4]{2})^3$

(v) $\ (2^{1/2})^4 = (\sqrt{2})^4 = 2^2 = 4.$

2.4.3 Rationalization

Firstly it is necessary to appreciate what a *surd* is. It is a quantity which cannot be expressed in terms of finite terms of ordinary numbers, hence the mathematical term *irrational*. This may be a little difficult to understand but we might approach the problem by considering square roots. Those which cannot be further reduced fall into this category, e.g. $\sqrt{2}$ is a surd because it cannot be reduced. On the other hand $\sqrt{8}$ is not a surd because it can be reduced to $2\sqrt{2}$ as follows:

$$8 = 2 \times 2 \times 2 \qquad \therefore \ \sqrt{8} = \sqrt{2} \times \sqrt{2} \times \sqrt{2}$$

but $\qquad \sqrt{2} \times \sqrt{2} = 2$

hence $\qquad \sqrt{8} = 2\sqrt{2}.$

Other quantities which are surds are for example $\sqrt{3}$, $\sqrt{5}$, there are of course many more. Rationalization is the process of clearing surds within an expression, most easily explained through the following example.

Normally evaluation of $1/\sqrt{2}$ presents some difficulty (we assume that a scientific calculator is not to hand). However it can be multiplied by the fraction $\sqrt{2}/\sqrt{2}$ (which of course is equal to 1) as shown:

$$\frac{1}{\sqrt{2}} = \frac{1}{\sqrt{2}} \times \frac{\sqrt{2}}{\sqrt{2}} = \frac{\sqrt{2}}{2} = \frac{1.414}{2} = 0.707$$

Another example will be found in Section 3.1.3.

2.4.4 A Chat About Exponential Functions

So far all this looks straightforward but in all the cases and examples we have met the exponential is a *known* figure. Things tend to get more difficult when it is the unknown. However firstly let us decide what a *function* is. The word has a tendency to crop up frequently in mathematics so it is essential to be sure of what it means. A function of anything may be described as something which varies when the 'anything' varies, e.g the statement that y is a function of x means that y must vary when x does, i.e. the value of y at any instant depends on the value taken by x. Mathematically we express this by $y = f(x)$ where f represents the function.

There are many examples of functions in daily life, for example, the cost of motoring is a function of the annual mileage, our abilities are a function of age, the time we take to read this page is a function of how quick we are at reading. Generally in $y = f(x)$, x is called the independent variable because it can assume different values, y is the *dependent variable* because it depends on the value of x.

An exponential function is simply one of the many kinds of function, it is an expression in which one of the variable quantities appears in the exponent of another quantity, e.g.

$$y = 12^x, \quad y = b^{3x}$$

28

These are just functions of x in which it is evident that if x is given various values, y will assume corresponding values. Now if an *unknown* quantity, x is to be raised to a *known* power, e.g. 3, this is straightforward because the answer is simply $x^3 = x \times x \times x$. However if on the other hand a quantity has to be raised to an unknown power (e.g. x, $3x$, etc.), then we are in trouble because for example, 12^x cannot be solved unless presumably we know the value of the unknown! Here are two examples:

$$2 = x^3 \quad \text{can be solved easily as} \quad x = \sqrt[3]{2} \quad (= 1.26)$$

but $2 = 3^x$ cannot be solved directly as the xth root of 2, i.e. from $\sqrt[x]{2} = 3$ (note that we can take the square, cube or x root in an equation provided that both sides of the equation are treated the same – see Chapter 3). Certainly x has now been shifted to a rather awkward place.

So, how can we solve this? Fortunately logarithms come to our aid as developed in the next Section. We will see that such awkward exponential functions can be reduced to a more easily handled algebraic form.

2.5 Logarithms

Calculations involving logarithms require the use of tables of logarithms also tables of antilogarithms (use of the latter may be avoided if some slight inconvenience is acceptable). These tables are easily obtained and are inexpensive, moreover they may still play an important role in electronic and allied calculations. However such a method of calculation is gradually being eclipsed by the electronic calculator although logarithms do have the advantage that no batteries are needed. The electronic calculator, especially if it is of the scientific variety, can carry out the same tasks in next to no time. However we should not avoid understanding logarithms even if most calculations are made the easy way with a calculator. Here therefore we look at the principle and use of logarithms on the assumption that the reader has 'log' and preferably also 'antilog' tables at hand.

From what has gone before in this Chapter we see that:

$$10^a \times 10^b = 10^{a+b} \quad \text{and} \quad 10^a \div 10^b = 10^{a-b}$$

On the left-hand side of each expression is multiplication or division, equalled in both cases on the right-hand side by a term involving addition or subtraction only. With large numbers or numbers with several decimal places, multiplication and division are much more difficult to carry out than addition and subtraction, thus a system which converts the former to the latter has much to recommend it. Tables of logarithms help us to do this with an accuracy more than sufficient for most work and it is assumed that the reader has such a book of Tables to hand. By means of the numbers 10 to 99 in the left-hand column in conjunction with those along the top of the table and also those in the difference column on the right, the logarithm of any number of up to four significant figures can be obtained.

In the calculations above, 10 is known as the *base* and a and b are exponents (as in Sect. 2.4). Any other number may be used for the base, but 10 has many advantages and is in general use. Logarithms to the base 10 are known as *common logarithms*. For certain purposes *Napierian* or *Natural logarithms* may be used, these are the original logarithms invented by John Napier and are less easy to get on with because they are to a base denoted by ε (Greek, epsilon), which we meet later in Section 2.5.4. They have special use with certain mathematical functions and series but here we recognize that ε is a rather awkward decimal, 2.718, 281.....which never ends.

We already know from Section 1.2.6 that, for example, 1, 10, 100, 1000....may also be written as 10^0, 10^1, 10^2, 10^3....The common logarithm is simply the exponent in each case so that:

the logarithm of 1   is 0
(also the logarithm of 0.1 is -1)
the logarithm of 10   is 1
(the logarithm of 0.01 is -2 and so on)
the logarithm of 100   is 2
the logarithm of 1000   is 3

What we have yet to determine are the values between 1 and 10, 10 and 100, etc. These we obtain from the logarithm tables mentioned above. These give the exponent (i.e. logarithm) for all values from 1 to 9.999, for example:

the logarithm of 2 is 0.3010
(shown against 20), meaning that $10^{0.3010} = 2$,

and

the logarithm of 9 is 0.9542
(shown against 90), meaning that $10^{0.9542} = 9$,

and using the four-figure tables to the full, the logarithm of 5.647 is 0.7518, hence $10^{0.7518} = 5.647$. This is read horizontally from 56 in the left-hand column and in the main column under 4, giving the logarithm for 5640 as 0.7513. To this must be added the figure given under 7 in the right-hand columns which in this case is 5, hence the logarithm of 5.647 is read as 0.7513 + 5, i.e. 0.7518.

Now if we need the logarithm of say, 56.47 which is ten times 5.647, recalling that a logarithm is simply the exponent and that multiplying by 10 adds 1 to the exponent, then we automatically have the logarithm for 56.47 as 0.7518 + 1 = 1.7518.

From this it is clear that because 5.647 lies between 1 and 10, its logarithm must be greater than 0 but less than 1. Similarly log 56.47 must be greater than 1 but less than 2 and the log of 564.7 must be between 2 and 3. For those who need practice and have logarithm tables to hand, it is suggested that logarithms of the following should be found, the answers are given in brackets:

8042 (3.9054)   26 (1.4150)
26.2 (1.4183)   562.8 (2.7503)
71892 (4.8566)

Note that in the last case the logarithm of a 5-figure number is required, ordinary logarithm tables are 4-figure (7-figure are also available but we shall seldom need the greater accuracy of these). Accordingly in this particular case, the units figure of 2 must be ignored, i.e. the logarithm of 71890 is obtained.

31

Straightforward so far but now we come to the part where some confusion may arise. This is in finding and manipulating logarithms of numbers less than 1. The rules show that dividing by 10, 100....reduces the logarithm by 1, 2...., and taking one of the examples above:

log 26	= 1.4150	
log 2.6 (i.e. 26×10^{-1})	= 1.4150 – 1	= 0.4150
log 0.26 (i.e. 26×10^{-2})	= 1.4150 – 2	

(or equally 0.4150 – 1) and this would be equal to –0.5850.

This is quite correct but now a new set of tables is required for logarithms of numbers less than 1. Such an extra set of tables is cunningly avoided by considering logarithms as being made up of two separate parts, the *characteristic* which is the part before the decimal point and can be positive, negative or zero and the *mantissa*, the group of four figures after the decimal point and which is always positive. So that there is no confusion with a negative characteristic, the minus sign is placed above the number, not preceding it, for this would make the *whole* logarithm negative. So we write log 0.26 not as –0.5850 but as $\overline{1}.4150$, remembering that this is actually equivalent to –1 + 0.4150. $\overline{1}, \overline{2}, \overline{3}...$ we express as 'bar 1, bar 2, bar 3, etc. Here are two examples;

$$\log 0.026 = \overline{2}.4150 \qquad \log 0.0026 = \overline{3}.4150$$

Summing this up: if a number is greater than 1, then the characteristic is positive and it is one less than the number of figures to the left of the decimal point. If the number is less than 1, then the characteristic is negative and it is one more than the number of noughts to the right of the decimal point. Here are some examples:

Logarithm	of 3	is 0.4771,
	of 300	it is 2.4771
	of 0.3	it is $\overline{1}.4771$
and	of 0.0003	it is $\overline{4}.4771$.

2.5.1 Multiplication

To multiply two or more numbers together, we simply add their logarithms to obtain the logarithm of the product. The number which corresponds to this logarithm (the antilogarithm) is the answer.

Antilogarithms are usually supplied as a second table to logarithms, they speed the work although are not essential because the logarithm table itself can be used in the inverse manner, that is by searching through the logarithms to find the number corresponding.

Here is an example of multiplication:

Multiply 9 by 4 :

$$\begin{array}{lll} \log 9 & = 0.9542 \\ \log 4 & = \underline{0.6021} \\ \log (9 \times 4) & = 1.5563 & \text{(antilog. } 0.5563 = 3599). \end{array}$$

Now in converting a logarithm back into its number, a positive or zero characteristic indicates that the number of figures to the left of the decimal point is equal to (characteristic +1). If the characteristic is negative, then the number of noughts to the right of the decimal point is equal to (characteristic −1).

From this, with a positive characteristic of 1, we must place the decimal point so that there are 2 figures to its left, i.e. antilog 1.5563 = 35.99. The correct answer is of course, 36 which shows that 4-figure logarithms do allow some inaccuracy to creep in. However note that there appears to be a slight irregularity here for if we had obtained the antilogarithm of 1.5563 from the *logarithm* tables, the correct answer would have been given. This is of little consequence because it is evident that small inaccuracies are a risk we take in working to 4 figures only. In fact with 7-figure logarithms, the answer given is 36.00020, very much better.

The convenience of logarithms becomes apparent in the next example:

Multiply 8.624 by 0.02853 by 26.42

```
log. 8.624    =   0.9357
log. 0.02853  =   2̅.4553
log. 26.42    =   1.4219
                  ────────
                  0.8129
```

The three mantissas add up to 1.8129 so +1 is carried over to add to the characteristics hence giving a total of 0 (remember that the logarithm of 0.02853 is really −2 + 0.4553. Antilogarithm tables give 6500 for 0.8129, hence the final answer is 6.500.

2.5.2 Division

To divide, subtract the logarithms to obtain the logarithm of the quotient. Let us start with an easy one - divide 39 by 13:

```
log 39       =  1.5911
log 13       =  1.1139
             ─────────
log 39/13    =  0.4772
```

antilog 0.4772 = 3.0 which we know to be correct.

Now for two more examples:

(i) Divide 0.862 by 0.03142

```
log 0.8620       =  1̅.9355
log 0.03142      =  2̅.4972
                 ──────────
log of quotient  =  1.4383
```

note with regard to the characteristics, subtracting −2 from −1 gives −1 − (−2), i.e. −1 + 2 = +1.

antilog 1.4383 = 27.44.

(ii) Evaluate $\dfrac{19.635 \times 0.0008781}{10^6}$

We now have a problem because 19.635 contains 5 figures and we are using 4-figure logarithms. A little guesswork is required – log 19.630 = 1.2930 and log 19.640 = 1.2932, therefore the

34

log of 19.635 can be estimated as 1.2931.

$$
\begin{array}{ll}
\text{log } 19.635 & = 1.2931 \\
\text{log } 0.0008781 & = \underline{\overline{4}.9435} \\
\text{log of numerator} & = \overline{2}.2366 \\
\text{log } 10^6 & = \underline{6.0000} \\
\text{log of quotient} & = \overline{8}.2366
\end{array}
$$

hence quotient = antilog $\overline{8}.2366$ = 1.724×10^{-8} and we note how easily powers of 10 fit into the system.

Finally in this Section, here is a practical example:

We wish to calculate the resistance per metre of fine silver wire 0.1 mm diameter (d). The resistivity of silver (ρ) is 0.016 $\times 10^{-6}$ ohm-metres (see also Sect. 3.1.8.).

Area of cross section of wire =

$$
a = \pi \times \frac{0.1^2}{4} = \frac{\pi \times 0.01}{4} = \frac{0.31416}{4} = 0.007854 \text{ mm}^2
$$

$$
= 0.007854 \times 10^{-6} \text{ m}^2
$$

(no need for logarithms yet).

Then resistance

$$
= \rho/a = \frac{0.016 \times 10^{-6}}{0.007854 \times 10^{-6}} = \frac{0.016}{0.007854}
$$

now we need logarithms:

$$
\begin{array}{ll}
\text{log } 0.016 & = \overline{2}.2041 \\
\text{log } 0.007854 & = \underline{\overline{3}.8951} \\
\text{log of quotient} & = 0.3090
\end{array}
$$

for which the antilog = 2.037 ohms.

2.5.3 Powers and Roots

To calculate the value of the power of a number, multiply its logarithm by the exponent to obtain the logarithm of the

35

answer.

To calculate the value of the root of a number, divide its logarithm by the exponent to obtain the logarithm of the answer.

As an example, find, using logarithms the value of 2^3:

$$\log 2 \qquad = 0.3010$$
$$\log 2^3 \qquad = 0.3010 \times 3 = 0.9030$$

then, antilog $0.9030 = 7.998$ which is very nearly the correct answer of 8.

Here is an example which clearly demonstrates the usefulness of logarithms:

Calculate 0.08431^5

$$\log 0.08431 \qquad = \overline{2}.9259$$
$$\therefore \quad \log 0.08431^5 \qquad = \overline{2}.9259 \times 5$$

Remember that the characteristic is negative whereas the mantissa is positive. Deal with the latter first:

$$0.9259 \times 5 = 4.6295$$

giving a positive figure of 4 to be carried over into the characteristic which is also multiplied by 5 hence:

$$-2 \times 5 = -10, \quad \text{add in the 4 to give } -10 + 4 = -6.$$

This when combined with the mantissa results in $\overline{6}.6295$, the antilog of which is:

$$0.000004261 \quad \text{or} \quad 4.261 \times 10^{-6}.$$

Next let us calculate a cube root, e.g. $\sqrt[3]{0.4321}$

$$\log 0.4321 \qquad = \overline{1}.6356$$
$$\log \sqrt[3]{0.4321} \qquad = \frac{\overline{1}.6356}{3}$$

Now the characteristic and mantissa must be treated separately. The characteristic is always a whole number and to keep it so we manipulate the calculation as follows:

$\overline{1}.6356$ is the same as $-1 + 0.6356$ or $-3 + 2.6356,$

i.e. the characteristic has been increased by the smallest number so that it becomes exactly divisible by 3. In this case 2 has been subtracted from the -1 to make -3. By adding 2 to the mantissa no change has been made in the value of the complete logarithm and it is now divisible by 3:

$$\frac{-3 + 2.6356}{3} = -1 + 0.8785$$

written as $\overline{1}.8785,$ the antilog of which is 0.7560, i.e.

$$\sqrt[3]{0.4321} = 0.7560 .$$

There is another way of handling a negative characteristic which is not divisible exactly by the exponent, this is to convert the whole logarithm to a negative number, carry out the division required and finally convert back to normal logarithmic form so that antilog tables can be used. The above example is now calculated in this way:

$$\log 0.4321 = \overline{1}.6356 = -1 + 0.6356 = -0.3644$$

this is no longer in characteristic plus mantissa form but it is a single negative number which is divisible by any other number, so:

$$\frac{-0.3644}{3} = -0.1215$$

Reconverted this becomes $-1 + 0.8785$ or $\overline{1}.8785,$ the antilog of which is 0.7560.

* * * * *

We are now in a position to grapple with the problem discovered at the end of Section 2.4.3, i.e. how to solve such an expression as $2 = 3^x$

By taking logarithms of both sides:

$$\log 2 = x \log 3$$

$$\therefore \ x = \frac{\log 2}{\log 3} = \frac{0.3010}{0.4771} = 0.631 \text{ hence } 2 = 3^{0.631}$$

2.5.4 Change of Base

Things get a little more complicated here because we are now considering two different logarithm bases at the same time, the aim being to change between the two. We have now considered common (base 10) logarithms in some depth and also mentioned Napierian logarithms in Section 2.5, here therefore we develop formulae for changing between them. The process is the same for changing between any other bases.

Napierian logarithms have a rather complicated base which is the sum of a *series* (these are considered in more detail in Section 7.4 but the series is quoted here for interest) :

$$e = 1 + 1 + \frac{1}{2} + \frac{1}{2 \times 3} + \frac{1}{2 \times 3 \times 4} + \ \text{.......}$$

a never-ending series resulting in a sum to 5 figures of 2.7183. We use the letter e to denote this number and it is also used with Napierian logarithms to avoid confusion with common logarithms. Correctly, log N to the base 10 would be written $\log_{10} N$ but generally it is more simply expressed by log N. The Napierian (or natural) logarithm of N however is always written as $\log_e N$ to distinguish it from the common variety.

Consider first the general case in which it is required to change from logarithms calculated to a base a into another system in which the base is b. Take any number, N which has logarithms in the a system denoted by x and in the second system (b) by y. Accordingly:

$$N = a^x \text{ therefore } \log_a N = x$$

(the subscript denoting the logarithm system).

Next take logarithms to the base b of each side:

$$\log_b N = x \times \log_b a$$

hence
$$\log_b N = \log_a N \times \log_b a$$

and
$$\log_a N = \frac{\log_b N}{\log_b a}$$

From this we see that the logarithm of any number to the base a is equal to the logarithm of the same number to the base b divided to the logarithm of a to the base b.

Considering the relationship between common and Napierian logarithms:

$$\log_{10} N = \frac{\log_e N}{\log_e 10}$$

Now
$$\log_e 10 = 2.3026 \text{ approx.}$$

hence
$$\log_e N = \log_{10} N \times 2.3026$$

Also
$$\log_{10} N = \frac{\log_e N}{2.3026} = \log_e N \times 0.4343 \text{ approx.}$$

Hence to convert common into Napierian logarithms, multiply by 2.3026 (more accurately, 2.302,585,1). To convert Napierian into common logarithms, multiply by 0.4343.

Undoubtedly this requires more than a little concentration because we are equating and switching between logarithm bases. First a reminder:

Since
$$\log_e 10 = 2.3026$$

then
$$e^{2.3026} = 10.$$

From this any number which is a power of 10 can also be expressed as a power of e. Thus:

$$\log 17.6 = 1.2455$$

hence $\quad 17.6 = 10^{1.2455} = e^{(2.3026 \times 1.2455)} = e^{2.8679}$

and therefore $\quad \log_e 17.6 = 2.8679.$

Next, without using Napierian logarithms, calculate the value of $\log_e 3$:

$\log_e 3 = \log_{10} 3 \times 2.3026 = 0.4771 \times 2.3026 = 1.0986.$

Chapter 3

ALGEBRA

Algebra may be described as a branch of mathematics which manipulates letters of the alphabet to stand for numbers whose values are not known. It enables us to design mathematical statements which we call *equations*. These can then be solved using known rules so that ultimately numbers can be allocated to the hitherto unknowns to obtain a number result.

Many processes in science and engineering can be reduced to a set of algebraic equations, the solution of which enables the process to be understood better and its outcome to be predicted.

Algebra is in no way a recent development, a form was in use nearly 4,000 years ago in ancient Egypt, however the technique more or less as we know it today, was developed much later. In fact the name algebra was derived from the Arabic, *al-jabr*, literally translated as meaning 'the reunion of fragments'. We will find that this is not an unreasonable description of the process.

3.1 Algebraic Expressions

We might define an algebraic expression as a collection of symbols expressing a hitherto unknown quantity. Care must be taken to ensure that similar terms are kept together to the exclusion of all others. This means that all a^2 terms may be combined into a single term, all a terms similarly and of course all terms consisting of a number only. Accordingly an expression such as $a^2 + 6a - 27 - 3a$ can only be simplified by combining the two terms $6a$ and $-3a$ $(= 3a)$, the a^2 and -27 stand on their own and cannot be combined with anything else.

As a further example we can take the sum (i.e. the amount resulting from addition) of:

$$5a^3, \ -3, \ 6a^2, \ -27, \ 4a, \ -3a^2$$

These terms should be grouped in descending powers of a, i.e.

$$5a^3 \qquad +6a^2 - 3a^2 \qquad +4a \qquad -3 \; -27$$

to result in $\quad 5a^3 + 3a^2 + 4a - 30.$

3.1.1 Addition and Subtraction

Addition is accomplished simply by adding similar or like terms. As an example, to find the sum of $5a^3 + 3a^2 + 4a - 30$ and $6a^3 + 2a^2 - 7a - 21$, the two expressions may be set out as follows with similar terms in the same columns:

$$
\begin{array}{r}
5a^3 + 3a^2 + 4a - 30 \\
6a^3 + 2a^2 - 7a - 21 \\
\hline
11a^3 + 5a^2 - 3a - 51
\end{array}
$$

which is the result of adding the two expressions, however with a little more experience the sum might be written down directly. Not so perhaps with the next example in which we add $5x^3 + 4x^2 + 5$ to $3x^3 - 8x^2 + x - 3$ and $2x^2 - 3x + 15$.

Setting these expressions down and adding:

$$
\begin{array}{r}
5x^3 + 4x^2 \qquad\;\; + 5 \\
3x^3 - 8x^2 + x - 3 \\
2x^2 - 3x + 15 \\
\hline
\end{array}
$$

we get $\quad 8x^3 - 2x^2 - 2x + 17$

and note the spaces left where no term of the particular power exists.

Note that there is nothing significant in our changing from a and b to x and y. Generally in mathematics we seem to prefer letters from the beginning or end of the alphabet although in electronics letters are often chosen which have some relationship with the quantity represented.

Subtraction can be carried out in a similar way although when only two expressions are involved, the answer might be written down directly. Failing this the expressions may be set out as above with normal subtraction following. However if the signs of all terms in the bottom line are changed, then addition takes the place of subtraction, e.g.

Subtract $5x^3 + 3x^2 + 4x - 30$ from $6x^3 + 2x^2 - 7x - 21$

$$
\begin{array}{r}
6x^3 + 2x^2 - 7x - 21 \\
-5x^3 - 3x^2 - 4x + 30 \quad \text{(signs changed over)} \\
\hline
x^3 - x^2 - 11x + 9 \quad \text{(by addition)}
\end{array}
$$

3.1.2 Multiplication and Division

Here it is important not to let error creep in because signs have become muddled. The reminders below may help and we see that when a minus is around it takes preference over a plus except when two minus signs are involved, then the result is a plus as shown :

$$+ \times + = + \qquad + \times - = -$$

$$- \times + = - \qquad - \times - = +$$

With fractions the same applies:

when both numerator and denominator are plus, the fraction is plus

when either numerator or denominator is minus, the fraction is minus

when both numerator and denominator are minus, the fraction is plus.

As an example, simplify $16x \times -3y$.

The numbers are first multiplied, i.e. $16 \times -3 = -48$. Then x is multiplied by y, giving xy, so the result is $-48xy$.

Next simplify $\dfrac{21x}{-7y}$

43

From the rule above, with the denominator minus, the whole fraction becomes minus, so we have:

$$\frac{-21x}{7y} \quad \text{which cancels to} \quad \frac{-3x}{y}$$

More terms can be handled in the same way but it might be more convenient to work in stages, e.g.

Evaluate $\qquad -2a \times -5b \times -15c$

Taking the first two terms only:
$$-2a \times -5b = 10ab$$

and then involving the third term:
$$10ab \times -15c = -150abc$$

3.1.3 Brackets

In algebra we will find the constant use of brackets. They seem to pop-up everywhere and so they should because they have an important purpose. Brackets always come in pairs. If there is an opening bracket [( ] anywhere, there must be its closing bracket [ )] later on in the expression. Whatever lies within a pair of brackets must be treated with respect.

A term outside of a bracketed quantity operates on each term within the brackets when the latter are removed, e.g. $7(6a + 2b)$ becomes $42a + 14b$ without the brackets. When bracketed quantities are multiplied together and the first bracket contains more than one term, the second bracket terms are multiplied by each of the first bracket terms, e.g. as follows:

$$(a + b)(c + d) = a(c + d) + b(c + d) = ac + ad + bc + bd$$

$$(a - b)(c + d) = a(c + d) - b(c + d) = ac + ad - bc - bd$$

We can expand the following for practice:

$$(a + b)^2 = (a + b)(a + b) = a(a + b) + b(a + b) = a^2 + 2ab + b^2.$$

$$(a - b)^2 = (a - b)(a - b) = a(a - b) - b(a - b) = a^2 - 2ab + b^2$$

and here we note that $-b \times -b = +b^2$. Here is another very useful one:

$$(a + b)(a - b) = a(a - b) + b(a - b) = a^2 - b^2$$

as an example the solution of $593^2 - 591^2$ simply becomes $(593 + 591)(593 - 591)$, i.e. $1184 \times 2 = 2368$.

The process can be reversed because quantities having a common factor may be bracketed with the factor placed outside, e.g. $6a^2 + 2ab$ has the common factor $2a$, hence we can write this expression as $2a(3a + b)$.

The last formula above enables us to examine rationalization (Sect. 2.4.3) again, e.g. by simplifying

$$\frac{1}{\sqrt{3} - \sqrt{2}}.$$

Using this formula, the denominator of the expression can be turned into the difference of two squares, i.e.:

$$\frac{1}{\sqrt{3} - \sqrt{2}} = \frac{1}{(\sqrt{3} - \sqrt{2})} \times \frac{\sqrt{3} + \sqrt{2}}{(\sqrt{3} + \sqrt{2})} =$$

$$= \frac{\sqrt{3} + \sqrt{2}}{(\sqrt{3})^2 - (\sqrt{2})^2} = \frac{\sqrt{3} + \sqrt{2}}{3 - 2} = \sqrt{3} + \sqrt{2}$$

i.e. $1.732 + 1.414 = 3.146$.

3.1.4 Simplification of Algebraic Expressions

So far we have considered simple expressions and equations. Frequently the need will arise for simplification of what appears to be a rather extensive and complicated expression. There are three rules to guide us:

(i)   first simplify terms within brackets
(ii) carry out the necessary procedures to remove the brackets
(iii) collect together similar terms

As an example, simplify:

$$8\,(12x^2 + 3x - 2) - 5x(2x + 3 - 5x) + 21$$

The second bracketed quantity can clearly be reduced to $(3 - 3x)$ so expanding and removing brackets, we get:

$$96x^2 + 24x - 16 - 15x + 15x^2 + 21,$$

and collecting like terms:

$$111x^2 + 9x + 5$$

Now if we substitute any value for x (e.g. 3, 4 or 5) the original and simplified expressions give the same answer — a useful check.

A slightly more complicated expression involving brackets within brackets might be:

$$21x\,\{5x^2 + 8x(x - 3) - 4(3x^2 - 13x + 7) + 18\}$$

there are now two kinds of brackets and it is obvious that ( ) must be resolved before { }. We cannot simplify the terms within the internal brackets so the next step is to remove them:

$$21x\{5x^2 + 8x^2 - 24x - 12x^2 + 52x - 28 + 18\}$$

which by collecting like terms becomes:

$$21x\{x^2 + 28x - 10\}$$

which can either be left like this or expanded to:

$$21x^3 + 588x^2 - 210x$$

Again, check by substituting a small number for x.

3.1.5 *Factors and Factorization*

A factor is a term in an algebraic expression which divides exactly into the expression, i.e it does not leave a remainder.

In simplest terms, in the expression $ab + bc$, b is the *common* factor because all terms contain b, hence this can be tidied up as $b(a + c)$. Similarly 5 is a common factor of $15x + 25y$, resulting in $5(3x + 5y)$ – and note that the change in both cases does not leave a remainder.

In the slightly more complex expression $16x^4 + 24x^3 - 32x^2 + 4x$ it is evident that $4x$ is a common factor. The expression can therefore be rearranged as $4x(4x^3 + 6x^2 - 8x + 1)$ and no more common factors can be found.

Factorization is therefore the process of extracting the factors, if any, of an algebraic expression. Take for example, the expression $11x^2 - 17$, it is immediately evident that here factorization is not possible, meaning that the expression contains no common factor. In more complex expressions we may need to extract the *highest common factor* (h.c.f.). Much of this may have to be carried out by inspection, for example in the expression $21x^2 - 7$, the h.c.f. is clearly 7, resulting in $7(3x^2 - 1)$.

Now things get more difficult, e.g. factorize $10x^2 + 11x - 6$.

For us this is a case of trial and error. For a computer the same although with the whole job completed in less than one second.

We firstly have the choice of splitting up the $10x^2$. There are two possibilities, $10x \times x$ and $5x \times 2x$. The -6 can be split up into its factors as -6×1, 6×-1, -3×2, 3×-2. Accordingly there are numerous possibilities, only one of which is correct. They must be tried out one by one until hopefully one succeeds, e.g

$$(10x - 6)(x + 1)$$

i.e. $\qquad 10x(x + 1) - 6(x + 1) = 10x^2 + 4x - 6$

(we are looking for a second term of $+11x$ – try again)

$$(10x + 6)(x - 1) = 10x^2 - 4x - 6 \quad – \text{ no good}$$

47

until.... $(5x-2)(2x+3) = 10x^2 + 11x - 6$

so these are the required factors.

This is a seemingly laborious task, however with experience many trials can be seen to be hopeless merely by inspection and therefore time is not wasted on them.

We have in fact already used factorization as examples in Section 3.1.3. Here are some more useful ones, each comprising two factors:

$$a^3 + b^3 = (a+b)(a^2 - ab + b^2)$$

$$a^3 - b^3 = (a-b)(a^2 + ab + b^2)$$

3.1.6 Remainder Theorem

This is a theorem which is useful for checking whether a particular factor in an expression is valid (in fact it is also known as the *Factor Theorem*). It states that if for example, $(x-a)$ is a factor then substitution of $x = a$ in the expression must result in zero. Equally therefore if $(x+a)$ is a factor, then substitution of $x = -a$ must also result in zero. Take as an example the expression $x^2 + x - 6$. It factorizes into $(x-2)(x+3)$. By the Remainder Theorem therefore substitution of either $x = 2$ or $x = -3$ in the expression should result in zero and this is easily checked.

As a further check, for the expression $10x^2 + 11x - 6$ in Section 3.1.5, we have obtained the two factors $(5x-2)$ and $(2x+3)$. According to the Theorem therefore, substituting $x = 2/5$ and $x = -3/2$ should both produce a zero result and this is so, hence verifying the earlier work.

3.1.7 Fractional Expressions

Troublesome though these may appear at first, much can be done to simplify them. The first thing to look for is some commonality between the denominators, especially when the signs of one or more fractions can be changed around e.g. by multiplying both numerator and denominator by -1. It also makes sense to rearrange an expression to ensure that the cyclic order is correct, e.g. for three unknowns a, b and c, this is the order in which they should be arranged with a following c, for example:

$$\frac{a}{(a-b)(a-c)} + \frac{b}{(b-c)(b-a)}$$

requires the denominator of the second fraction to be rearranged to

$$- \frac{b}{(a-b)(b-c)}$$

(by multiplying both numerator and denominator by -1).

This is immediately helpful because $(a-b)$ now appears in both denominators. Hence:

$$\frac{a}{(a-b)(a-c)} - \frac{b}{(a-b)(b-c)} = \frac{a(b-c) - b(a-c)}{(a-b)(a-c)(b-c)} =$$

$$= - \frac{c(a-b)}{(a-b)(a-c)(b-c)} \ .$$

Note that the denominator of this expression is the *Least Common Multiple* (LCM) i.e. the least quantity that contains two or more quantities some number of times without remainder, e.g. as 12 is the LCM of 2, 3 and 4.

As a further example, for simplification of

$$\frac{1}{x+a} + \frac{1}{a^2 - x^2} - \frac{1}{x-a}$$

the first step is to change the sign of the last fraction because as Section 3.1.3 shows,

$$a^2 - x^2 = (a+x)(a-x),$$

so rearranging, the expression becomes:

$$\frac{1}{a+x} + \frac{1}{a^2-x^2} + \frac{1}{a-x}$$

and clearly the LCM is $a^2 - x^2$, resulting in

$$\frac{a-x+1+a+x}{a^2-x^2} = \frac{2a+1}{a^2-x^2}$$

3.1.8 Proportionals

There are many occasions in electronics when it is required to state how one thing varies with changes in another on which it is dependent. As an example, in considering the resistance of a conductor of uniform gauge, it is found that the resistance (R) is *directly proportional* to the conductor length (l) but *inversely proportional* to its cross-sectional area (a).

Put more mathematically,

$$R \propto l$$

where α (Greek, *alpha*) indicates direct proportionality

also

$$R \propto \frac{1}{a}$$

the $1/a$ indicating inverse proportionality.

Hence, combining the two, $R \propto l/a$ means that the resistance R is directly proportional to (varies as) the length of the conductor but inversely proportional to (varies inversely as) the area of cross-section.

This is useful information but it does not allow calculations to proceed. What is needed is a *constant of proportionality* for only with this can we change the 'varies as' sign (α) to an equals sign (=). With resistivity a constant is used for a particular material, usually designated by the Greek ρ (*rho*), hence:

$$R = \rho \frac{l}{a}$$

and knowing the value of ρ and the length and cross-sectional area of the conductor, its resistance can be calculated.

As an example, suppose we wish to calculate the resistance of 10 metres of copper wire of diameter 0.2 mm, $\rho = 1.60$ microhms (10^{-6} ohms) per centimetre.

Cross-sectional area $= \pi r^2 = \pi \times 10^{-2}$ sq mm $= \pi \times 10^{-4}$ sq cm.

$$l = 10 \times 10^2 = 10^3 \text{ cm.}$$

Then resistance,

$$R = \frac{1.60 \times 10^3}{\pi \times 10^{-4}} \text{ microhms} = \frac{1.60 \times 10}{\pi} \text{ ohms} = 5.092 \text{ ohms.}$$

Another example arises when we try to calculate the mutual inductance between two adjacent coils. For full 100% coupling (i.e. all the magnetic flux of one coil cutting all the turns of the second coil), we have:

$$M = \sqrt{(L_1 L_2)}$$

where M is the mutual inductance and L_1 and L_2 are the inductances of the coupled coils. However there is never 100% coupling so we write:

$$M \; \alpha \; \sqrt{(L_1 L_2)}$$

which still does not allow for practical calculations, so it is necessary to introduce a constant of proportionality (in this case, k), hence:

$$M = k \sqrt{(L_1 L_2)}$$

so knowing the value of k in any case, we can calculate M. Remember that without the k, the proportional sign α must be used.

3.2 Algebraic Equations

Much of mathematics revolves around the 'equals' (=) sign, defined by the dictionary as "the same in number, size, value, degree etc.". Mathematical equations have two parts separated by the equals sign and for convenience we refer to the left-hand side (l.h.s.) and the right-hand side (r.h.s.). When an equation has been set up, any operation which does not change the equality existing between the two sides is permissible, any which does destroy the equality is not – unless the equals sign is replaced for example by $\approx$ (approximately equal to) or $\neq$ (not equal to). Many problems in electronics can be reduced to a set of algebraic equations and the problem is then of discovering how to solve them.

Common operations are:

(i)   multiplication of both sides by the same quantity
(ii)   division of both sides by the same quantity
(iii)   addition of the same quantity to both sides
(iv)   subtraction of the same quantity from both sides
(v)   squaring both sides
(vi)   taking the square root of both sides.

3.2.1 Simple Equations

We can use a well known electronics formula as an example of the simple equation i.e. an equation having one unknown only. This allows us to calculate the charge (Q) on a capacitor of known capacitance (C) when a known voltage (V) is applied:

$$Q \text{ (coulombs)} = C \text{ (farads)} \times V \text{ (volts)}$$

From $Q = CV$ we can from (ii) above divide both sides of the equation by C to find the voltage appearing across a capacitor when only the charge and the capacitance are known. We simply divide both sides by the same quantity C to give:

$$\frac{Q}{C} = \frac{CV}{C}$$

here the C's cancel on the r.h.s., leaving us with

$$\frac{Q}{C} = V \; .$$

In the same way, by dividing both sides of the basic equation $Q = CV$ by V, we get:

$$\frac{Q}{V} = \frac{CV}{V} \quad \text{so by cancelling,} \quad \frac{Q}{V} = C.$$

From this it is evident that in this threesome, given the value of any two of the quantities, the value of the third can be determined.

Again we use a simple equation to determine the resistance in ohms at the higher temperature of 20°C of a length of copper wire when its resistance at 0°C is known to be 5 ohms. The formula is:

$$R_t \approx R_0 (1 + \alpha t)$$

the $\approx$ sign is used (see above) because this is a shortened form of the full equation, i.e. additional terms are required for greater accuracy. Generally the equation shown is sufficient for most investigations.

Here R_t is the resistance at the higher temperature, R_0 is the resistance at 0°C and α is the Temperature Coefficient of Resistance. For copper α is 0.0039, t is the rise in temperature which in this case is 20°C. From the formula:

$$R_t = 5 (1 + 0.0039 \times 20) = 5 (1.078) = 5.39 \text{ ohms.}$$

Note again that there is only one unknown (R_t).

* * * * *

Another useful technique is known as *cross-multiplication*, in which we multiply across the equals sign, i.e. if

$$\frac{a}{b} = \frac{c}{d}$$

then by cross-multiplication,

$$ad = bc$$

This is clearly equivalent to, but quicker than multiplying both sides by bd:

$$\frac{a}{b} = \frac{c}{d} \quad \therefore \quad \frac{abd}{b} = \frac{cbd}{d} \quad \therefore \quad ad = bc.$$

It is also possible to change over numerators and denominators on both sides for if as shown above, $bc = ad$, then dividing both sides by ac gives:

$$\frac{b}{a} = \frac{d}{c}.$$

3.2.2 Simultaneous Equations

These involve two or more variables which must have the same values in each equation. Simultaneous equations do not contain squares or roots of unknown quantities, hence are described as *linear*. Those which do involve such quantities are known as *quadratic equations* and are discussed in the next Section.

In the simplest of cases, i.e. when there are two independent equations, only one pair of values satisfies both equations. It is a golden rule that the number of equations required is the same as the number of unknowns. There are several methods by which simultaneous equations can be solved but perhaps the most illustrative is by a simple graph (graphs are considered in more detail in the next Chapter). Graphs of this type of equation (i.e. no terms are raised to any power) are always straight lines so only two points are needed to determine the graph of each expression.

Take for example the simultaneous equations $x + 2y = 8$ and $4x + 2y = 17$.

For $x + 2y = 8$, when $x = 0$, $y = 4$ and when $y = 0$, $x = 8$

for $4x + 2y = 17$, when $x = 0$, $y = 8.5$ and when $y = 0$, $x = 4.25$.

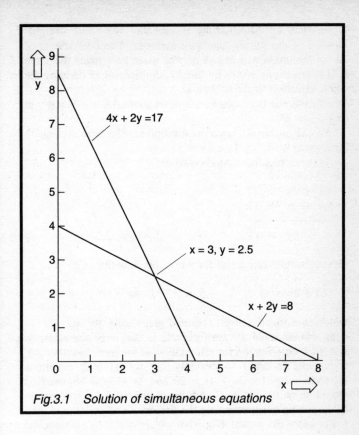

Fig.3.1   Solution of simultaneous equations

Given only these two points per expression, the graphs can be drawn as shown in Figure 3.1 and where they cross is the answer we are seeking for only at this point ($x = 3$, $y = 2.5$) are both equations together satisfied. This can be checked by substituting these values for x and y in the original equations.

When the two lines do not intersect, there is no solution, i.e. values for x and y which satisfy both equations together do not exist.

It is now clear that the term simultaneous also indicates that all the equations must be used together to obtain a solution.

Solution by Elimination is probably the most straightforward of the purely algebraic methods. The coefficients of one of the unknowns (e.g. x or y or z, etc.) are made the same in both equations in turn by suitably multiplying or dividing the whole equation as shown below.

Consider the two equations as used above, i.e. $x + 2y = 8$ and $4x + 2y = 17$.

We can eliminate, say x by multiplying the first expression throughout by 4, i.e. $4x + 8y = 32$.

Next subtract the second equation:

$$\begin{array}{rcl} 4x + 8y &=& 32 \\ 4x + 2y &=& 17 \\ \hline 6y &=& 15 \end{array} \qquad \therefore \ y = 2.5$$

Next substitute this result for y in either equation, e.g.

$$4x + 2y = 17 \ \therefore \ 4x + 5 = 17 \ \therefore \ 4x = 12 \ \therefore \ x = 3.$$

which confirms the result obtained graphically above.

In this example we are fortunate in that only one equation needed multiplication for elimination of the term containing x. It is quite in order to multiply (or divide) both equations separately, e.g. for $3x + 4y = 20$ and $2x + 5y = 25$, the first would be multiplied by 2 and the second by 3 for elimination of the x term or alternatively the first by 5 and the second by 4 to eliminate the y term. Note that we are breaking no rules, the equality in each equation is maintained throughout and it is evident that addition or subtraction of complete equations, one from the other, is also permissible.

Solution by Substitution in this method the values of say, x and y are obtained by expressing one of the unknowns in terms of the other. As an example, using the two equations above as examples, if $x + 2y = 8$ then $y = (8 - x)/2$.

This is now substituted in the second equation $4x + 2y = 17$, giving:

$$4x + \frac{2(8 - x)}{2} = 17, \text{ i.e. } 4x + 8 - x = 17$$

$$\therefore \ 3x = 9 \quad \text{and} \quad x = 3.$$

Substituting $x = 3$ in either of the original equations results in $y = 2.5$.

We can go one step further by for example, finding a value for y in terms of x in <u>both</u> equations, subsequently equating the two values obtained, e.g.

$$x + 2y = 8 \qquad \text{hence} \quad y = \frac{8-x}{2}$$

$$4x + 2y = 17 \qquad \text{hence} \quad y = \frac{17-4x}{2}$$

Then $\dfrac{8-x}{2} = \dfrac{17-4x}{2}$ $\qquad \therefore \ 8-x = 17-4x$

$$\therefore \qquad\qquad 3x = 9 \quad \text{and} \quad x = 3.$$

Again substituting $x = 3$ in either equation leads to $y = 2.5$.

Next a teaser: Divide 177 into two parts so that one-third of the first part is greater by 3 than one-quarter of the second part.

Let x represent the first part and y the second part.

Then $x + y = 177$ and $y = 177 - x$

Also $\qquad\qquad \dfrac{x}{3} - 3 = \dfrac{y}{4}$

$$\therefore \ 4x - 36 = 3y$$

$$\therefore \ 4x - 36 = 531 - 3x \quad \therefore \ 7x = 567$$

hence $x = 81$ and therefore $y = 177 - x = 96$.

When confronted with three equations containing three unknowns the technique is therefore firstly to reduce the three equations to two containing two unknowns. Then as shown above, the two can be reduced to one only, containing one unknown. This is solved and then the remaining two equations by substitution.

Here is an example involving three equations. It is to find the currents flowing in a *Wheatstone Bridge* (after Sir Charles Wheatstone, a British scientist). This bridge is an important one in electronics because it enables us to find the values of a large range of resistances or impedances. Here we consider resistances only, they are far less complicated.

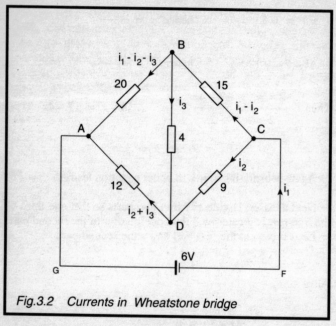

Fig.3.2   Currents in Wheatstone bridge

To see how the bridge functions we need two laws given to us by Gustav Robert Kirchhoff, a German physicist. Consider a practical bridge as shown in Figure 3.2. Kirchhoff's First Law effectively tells us that in any electrical network the current entering a point must be equal to the current leaving it, hence at point C:

Current in $= i_1$ current out $= i_2 + (i_1 - i_2)$

At point B

current in $= (i_1 - i_2)$ current out $= (i_1 - i_2 - i_3)$

At point D

current in and current out (i.e. D to A) $= (i_2 + i_3)$

Kirchhoff's Second Law states that in any closed electrical path (or *mesh*) the algebraic sum of the e.m.f.'s is equal to the algebraic sum of the products of the resistances and the respective currents in the separate parts. Note the term *algebraic*. We must first choose a direction of current flow which we consider as positive. Here we choose anticlockwise currents to be positive hence any arrow indicating currents in the opposite direction means that the current is treated as negative. From this:

Mesh AGFCDA:

$6 = 9i_2 + 12(i_2 + i_3)$ $\therefore 2 = 7i_2 + 4i_3$ (1)

which is our first equation.

Mesh DCBD:

$0 = 15(i_1 - i_2) + 4i_3 - 9i_2 \therefore 0 = 15i_1 - 24i_2 + 4i_3$ (2)

Mesh ADBA:

$0 = -4i_3 - 12(i_2 + i_3) + 20(i_1 - i_2 - i_3)$
$$\therefore 0 = 5i_1 - 8i_2 - 9i_3 \qquad (3)$$

Now we have our three equations containing three unknowns, a complete solution is therefore possible, e.g.

Multiply equation (3) by 3

$0 = 15i_1 - 24i_2 - 27i_3$ next subtract equation (2)
$0 = 15i_1 - 24i_2 + 4i_3$

to give $0 = \qquad\qquad -31i_3$

$\therefore i_3 = 0$ (in fact when $i_3 = 0$, the bridge is said to be balanced).

59

Next from (1)

$$i_2 = \frac{2 - 4i_3}{7} = \frac{2}{7} \quad \text{(amperes)}$$

and from (2)

$$0 = 15i_1 - \frac{24 \times 2}{7}$$

$$\therefore \quad i_1 = \frac{24 \times 2}{7 \times 15} = \frac{16}{35} \quad \text{amperes}$$

and from these three values for i_1, i_2 and i_3, currents in all branches can be calculated.

3.2.3 Quadratic Equations

Quadratic equations are those which involve the second but no higher power of an unknown quantity. The description comes from the Latin *quadrare* = to square. In contrast with simultaneous equations (Sect. 3.2.2) there is only one unknown but the fact that its square is involved leads to different methods of solution. The solutions are referred to as the *roots* of an equation and generally quadratic equations have two solutions but no more. There can however be a single root when the equation is in the form of a perfect square. Perhaps the simplest example is that of an equation containing only the square of the unknown quantity, i.e. there is no term containing the first power. Such an equation might be $x^2 - 25 = 0$ for then $x^2 = 25$ and $x = \pm 5$. We need the double sign $\pm$ because both $+5$ and -5 when squared result in 25.

An example of a *two-root* quadratic equation is given by $x^2 + 2x - 35 = 0$, the roots of which are $x = -7$ and $x = +5$. By substituting either of these values for x, we find that the net value of the left hand side is 0. An example of a *single root* quadratic containing also a first power of x is $x^2 + 8x + 16 = 0$ which has a single root, $x = -4$, no other.

These two types of equation are best illustrated by means of graphs as in Figure 3.3. Although the construction of these graphs is considered in detail in the next Chapter, illustrating the two equations here is useful to show how the roots can be obtained without recourse to mathematical manipulation. In essence x is given different values and at each the value of the

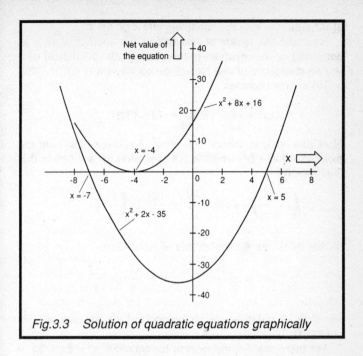

Net value of the equation

$x^2 + 8x + 16$

x = -4

x = -7

x = 5

$x^2 + 2x - 35$

Fig.3.3   Solution of quadratic equations graphically

complete equation is plotted. Where the curve crosses or touches the zero axis is the solution (as shown). For $x^2 + 2x - 35$ we would expect the curve to cross the zero axis twice but for $x^2 + 8x + 16$ it touches the axis only once because it is a perfect square. Note the similarity between the shapes of the two curves, somewhat different from the straight lines of simple equations (Fig. 3.1).

Here are three methods by which quadratic equations may be solved:

(i) *Completing the Square*

We take this step by step. Firstly if necessary, the equation must be simplified by dividing throughout by the coefficient of x^2, e.g. for the equation $2x^2 - 14x - 36 = 0$ we can clearly divide by 2 so leaving $x^2 - 7x - 18 = 0$. This is a simple example but it is also possible for the process to create fractions in the other terms. Then arrange all terms containing x and x^2 on the l.h.s.

of the equation with the remaining terms on the r.h.s.

Next add the *square* of one half of the coefficient of x to both sides of the equation. In this example the coefficient of x is 7 so the square of one half of the coefficient is $(7/2)^2$. The equation now becomes

$$x^2 - 7x + (7/2)^2 = 18 + (7/2)^2.$$

Note now that, as shown in Section 3.1.3, the l.h.s. is in the form $a^2 - 2ab + b^2$ which is the expansion of $(a - b)^2$. In this case therefore

$$\left(x - \frac{7}{2}\right)^2 = 18 + \frac{49}{4} = \frac{121}{4} = \left(\frac{11}{2}\right)^2$$

so that by taking the square root of both sides:

$$x - \frac{7}{2} = \pm \frac{11}{2} \qquad \therefore \ x = \frac{18}{2} \text{ or } \frac{-4}{2}$$

i.e. 9 or -2 and these are the two roots of the equation $x^2 - 7x - 18 = 0$.

For more practice the roots of the equation $x^2 + 2x - 35 = 0$ (Fig. 3.3) can be determined:

$$x^2 + 2x = 35$$

$$x^2 + 2x + 1 = 36$$

– add (half the coefficient of x)^2 to both sides

$$(x + 1)^2 = 36$$

$$x + 1 = \pm 6$$

$$\therefore \qquad x = 5 \text{ or } -7$$

as shown on the graph.

(2) *Solution by Factorization*

A solution here is only possible when the given equations can be resolved into factors. In this case the value of x which makes either of the factors vanish is one of the roots. To search for the factors, the equation must firstly be arranged in the standard form $ax^2 + bx + c = 0$. Taking as an example the equations quoted above:

factorizing $x^2 - 7x - 18 = 0$ gives $(x + 2)(x - 9) = 0$

then $x + 2 = 0$,   i.e. $x = -2$

also $x - 9 = 0$ i.e. $x = 9$

as already determined above by completing the square.

Also:

factorizing $x^2 + 2x - 35 = 0$ gives $(x - 5)(x + 7) = 0$

then $x - 5 = 0$ i.e. $x = 5$

also $x + 7 = 0$ i.e. $x = -7$.

All very straightforward but how in general can we find the factors (if any) of an expression? In fact it is mainly by trial and error. We could make a guess and then multiply both the terms in the second bracket by each of the terms in the first bracket, then repeat with other guesses until either we get an answer or alternatively give up. To assist in the process there is a simple way of seeing the wood for the trees which is by an adaptation of cross-multiplication, most easily described by examples.

(i) factorize $x^2 + 2x - 35 = 0$.

Start off with an arrangement as shown:

Now multiply vertically to determine the x^2 and numerical terms but diagonally for the x term. We have yet to add some numerical terms.

On the r.h.s. we next experiment with factors of 35, e.g.

x	35
x	1

Cross multiply and add to see whether by juggling signs it is possible to end up with $+2x$. Clearly here this cannot be done so next try

x	7
x	5

and now things look more promising. The only way to end up with $2x$ is for the 5 to be – and the 7 to be +, producing the factors $(x - 5)$ and $(x + 7)$ with the result $x = 5$ or -7.

Again, factorize $x^2 - 7x - 18 = 0$:

| x | 18 | ....no good,
|---|---|
| x | 1 |

| x | 6 | ....no good,
|---|---|
| x | 3 |

| x | 9 | ....this looks promising.
|---|---|
| x | 2 |

Next try the signs

| x | 9 | .... no good,
|---|---|
| x | -2 |

| x | -9 | ....perfect.
|---|---|
| x | 2 |

Hence the factors are $(x - 9)$ and $(x + 2)$, so $x = 9$ or -2.

For a little more practice, factorize $2x^2 - 23x - 39 = 0$. This results in

$2x$	3
x	-13

i.e. the factors are $(2x + 3)(x - 13)$ and $x = 13$ or $-\dfrac{3}{2}$.

(3) *Solution by Formula*
This is straightforward, remembering that the general quadratic equation structure must first be developed, i.e. in the form $ax^2 + bx + c = 0$. The method follows from the technique of completing the square as discussed in (1). From this general formula, dividing throughout by the coefficient of x^2, i.e. by a and transferring c to the r.h.s.,

$$x^2 + \frac{bx}{a} = \frac{-c}{a}$$

Next add the square of one half of the coefficient of x to both sides of the equation:

$$x^2 + \frac{bx}{a} + \frac{b^2}{4a^2} = \frac{-c}{a} + \frac{b^2}{4a^2}$$

$$\therefore \qquad \left\{ x + \frac{b}{2a} \right\}^2 = \frac{b^2 - 4ac}{4a^2}$$

and taking the square root of both sides:

$$x + \frac{b}{2a} = \frac{\pm \sqrt{(b^2 - 4ac)}}{2a}$$

hence

$$x = \frac{-b \pm \sqrt{(b^2 - 4ac)}}{2a}$$

Now if $b^2 > 4ac$, x will have two values or roots, with the curve to the equation cutting the axis at two points (Fig. 3.3 for $x^2 + 2x - 35$).

If $b^2 = 4ac$, the two roots are equal and the curve touches the axis (Fig. 3.3 for $x^2 + 8x + 16$)

If $b^2 < 4ac$, no real values satisfy the equation. The roots are said to be *imaginary* and we look at this description later.

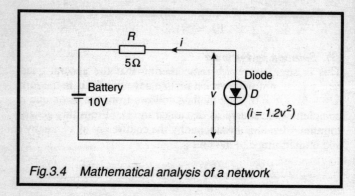

Fig.3.4   Mathematical analysis of a network

Here is a practical application of the solution of a quadratic by formula. Figure 3.4 shows what seems to be a simple electrical circuit. It is not so however because the resistance of the diode depends on the current through it. The difficulty therefore seems to be that the circuit resistance varies with the current which itself varies with the resistance. So how can we calculate the value of the current when the total circuit resistance is unknown?

The diode is known as a *non-linear* device which is one to which Ohm's Law does not apply. Generally its characteristic can be expressed by the current/voltage relationship, $i = kv^n$ where i is the current, v is the voltage, k is a constant and n is the *power index* of the material. We can use this relationship as an example when the characteristic obeys a square law, i.e. n = 2 so that $i = kv^2$.

In the circuit shown in Figure 3.4, a battery of 10V drives a current i through the series resistor, R and the diode, D. We assume k = 1.2, then:

66

$$i = 1.2v^2$$

The applied voltage is dropped across the resistor and the diode in series as shown, hence:

$$10 = iR + v = 5i + v$$

and since $i = 1.2v^2$,

$$10 = 5(1.2v^2) + v$$

so rearranging gives

$$6v^2 + v - 10 = 0$$

and we now have a quadratic equation which does not look as though it can be solved by factorization. Hence it must be solved by formula. Here $a = 6$, $b = 1$, $c = -10$, hence:

$$v = \frac{-1 \pm \sqrt{(1 - (-240)}}{12} = \frac{-1 \pm \sqrt{241}}{12} = \frac{-1 \pm 15.5242}{12}$$

i.e.
$$v = \frac{14.5242}{12} \quad \text{or} \quad \frac{-16.5242}{12} = 1.2104 \text{ or } -1.3770 \text{ (volts)},$$

then $\qquad i = 1.2v^2 = 1.7581$ or 2.2754 amperes.

Check: if $i = 1.7581$ amperes:

voltage across $R = i \times R = 1.7581 \times 5 = 8.7905$ volts
voltage across D $\qquad\qquad\qquad\qquad = 1.2104$ volts
$\qquad\qquad\qquad\qquad\qquad\qquad\qquad\overline{}$
$\qquad\qquad\qquad\qquad\qquad\qquad\quad 10.00$ volts,

the total voltage dropped in the circuit is therefore seen to be equal to that applied by the battery, hence the calculation is correct.

Similarly, if $i = 2.2754$ amperes:

voltage across R = 11.377 volts
voltage across D = −1.377 volts

the net voltage again is 10 volts, however although of course this solution is numerically correct, it is unacceptable because it suggests that the diode needs to set up an opposing voltage because the current is greater. Clearly in cases like this, although the quadratic produces two solutions, only one is acceptable.

(4) *The Relationship Between Coefficients and Roots*

So far, given a quadratic equation, we have been able to determine its roots. However it may also be required to form the original equation when the roots only are known. We have already found that by resolving the l.h.s. of a quadratic equation to its simplest form of factors, then the values of x which make either of these factors zero, are the values which satisfy the equation. Accordingly the roots of the equation $(x - \alpha)(x - \beta) = 0$ are α and β.

This can be expanded by multiplying out to obtain:

$$x^2 - (\alpha + \beta)x + \alpha\beta = 0 \tag{1}$$

From this it is evident that when the coefficient of x^2 is unity, the coefficient of x with its sign changed gives the <u>sum</u> of the roots while the constant term gives the <u>product</u> of the roots as follows.

Considering the general quadratic equation $ax^2 + bx + c = 0$, firstly divide throughout by a to make the coefficient of x^2 unity, then:

$$x^2 + \frac{bx}{a} + \frac{c}{a} = 0$$

which when compared with equation (1) above shows that:

$$\text{sum of roots} = (\alpha + \beta) = \frac{-b}{a}$$

$$\text{product of roots} = \alpha\beta = \frac{c}{a}$$

As an example let us discover the quadratic equation which has roots 4 and 2. Here then $\alpha = 4$, $\beta = 2$. The general equation which has roots α and β is as shown above:

$$(x - \alpha)(x - \beta) = 0 \quad \therefore (x - 4)(x - 2) = 0 \quad \therefore x^2 - 6x + 8 = 0$$

an easy one but now let us introduce a negative root, e.g. form the quadratic which has roots 4 and -2:

$$(x - \alpha)(x - \beta) = 0 \therefore (x - 4)\{x - (-2)\} = 0 \therefore x^2 - 2x - 8 = 0 .$$

Next, knowing that the sum of the roots of an equation is 8/3 and the product of the roots, 5/3, find the equation.

The equation is represented by $x^2 - (\alpha + \beta)x + \alpha\beta = 0$ and substituting:

$$x^2 - \frac{8x}{3} + \frac{5}{3} = 0$$

and multiplying throughout by 3 to avoid fractions:

$$3x^2 - 8x + 5 = 0 .$$

3.2.4 Setting Formulae to Work

From all that goes before in this Chapter we should now be in a position to manipulate formulae as we wish. Firstly, take a simple formula which considers the energy of a moving body:

$$\text{Kinetic energy (ke)} = 1/2 \, mv^2$$

where m is the mass and v the velocity of the body.

Suppose that, given the ke, we wish to find the velocity, then:

$$\text{ke} = 1/2 \, mv^2 \quad \text{i.e., } 2 \times \text{ke} = mv^2 \quad \therefore \frac{2 \times \text{ke}}{m} = v^2$$

hence

$$v = \sqrt{\frac{(2 \times \text{ke})}{m}}$$

by taking the square root if both sides.

Similarly, given the current in a radio transformer at a certain frequency as:

$$I = \frac{1}{2\sqrt{(R_p R_s)}}$$

where R_p and R_s are the resistances of the windings, how do we calculate the value of R_s when I and R_p are known?

$$2I = \frac{1}{\sqrt{(R_p R_s)}} \quad \therefore 4I^2 = \frac{1}{R_p R_s}$$

(squaring both sides),

$$\therefore \qquad 4I^2 \times R_p = \frac{1}{R_s}$$

(cross multiplying by R_p)

$$\therefore \qquad R_s = \frac{1}{4I^2 \times R_p}$$

* * * * *

Here is one dealing with the impedance at resonance of a series circuit. Z is the circuit impedance, R, X_L and X_C are the resistance and reactances involved. We wish to find the formula for X_C.

$$Z = \sqrt{\{R^2 + (X_L - X_C)^2\}}$$

$$\therefore \qquad Z^2 = R^2 + (X_L - X_C)^2$$

$$\therefore \qquad Z^2 - R^2 = (X_L - X_C)^2$$

$$\therefore \qquad \sqrt{(Z^2 - R^2)} = X_L - X_C$$

$$\therefore \qquad \sqrt{(Z^2 - R^2)} - X_L = -X_C$$

$$\therefore \qquad X_C = X_L - \sqrt{(Z^2 - R^2)}$$

– it is simply a case of applying the rules given earlier in the Chapter.

Chapter 4

GRAPHS

Graphs illustrate conditions pictorially and so are exceedingly useful in very many aspects of life. They appear everywhere and give their messages to readers in a form which often is easier to understand than by studying the appropriate equation or lists of figures. This gives a clue as to what graphs do, they show pictorially how one quantity varies as does another on which it is dependent, in a few words they show the relation between two variable quantities. The description *graph* seems to have arisen from the Greek, meaning *written*.

Renée Descartes (a French mathematician) was the first to publish the fact that any point on a plane can be defined relative to two axes by two numbers only – these are now known as *cartesian coordinates*. In electronics the two axes are almost invariably at right angles as shown in Figure 4.1 with the horizontal axis designated the x-axis and the vertical one, the y-axis. The position of any point in the area adjacent to the two axes can therefore be determined from the two coordinates. The distance of the point left or right from the y-axis is known as the *abscissa* (i.e. the coordinate measured parallel to the x-axis) whereas its distance above or below the x-axis (i.e. parallel to the y-axis) is known as the *ordinate*. If a point falls to the left of the y-axis then x is negative and at points below the x-axis, y is negative. This is illustrated in the Figure where in this case the position of point P is stated by the two numbers 4, 3 (abscissa, ordinate) as shown.

More generally it will be found that the terms x-coordinate and y-coordinate are used where the x-coordinate of a point is its distance left or right of the y-axis and the y-coordinate is its distance above or below the x-axis. As an example the coordinates of point Q are 2, -4 (x-coordinate, y-coordinate). It is perhaps easier to remember which is which using these labels.

The numbers in circles on the Figure indicate the *quadrant* and it will be seen that they run anti-clockwise which is usually the preferred direction in electronics, i.e. where there is a

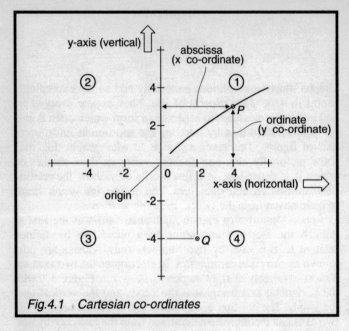

y-axis (vertical)

abscissa
(x co-ordinate)

②   4   ①

•P

2   ordinate
(y co-ordinate)

-4   -2   0   2   4

origin   x-axis (horizontal)

-2

③   -4   •Q   ④

Fig.4.1 Cartesian co-ordinates

choice, anti-clockwise is used in preference to clockwise. For most illustrations using graphs, quadrant 1 is sufficient, however as we progress it will be found that frequently in electronics, other quadrants up to all four are employed.

Note the *origin* at $x = 0$, $y = 0$. Scales on the two axes are of course chosen to suit the range to be plotted. Care must be taken here because frequently occasions arise when the two scales must be the same.

4.1 The Straight-Line Graph

We have already seen in Figure 3.1 straight lines plotted on a first quadrant graph. Such lines arise from *linear equations*, i.e. those in the form $ax + by + c = 0$. To plot such a graph is therefore straightforward because, knowing that it must result in a straight line, two points only need to be determined. Take as a simple example the equation $2x - 3y = 12$. Generally it is convenient to find the points on the line where $x = 0$ and also where $y = 0$. Then:

72

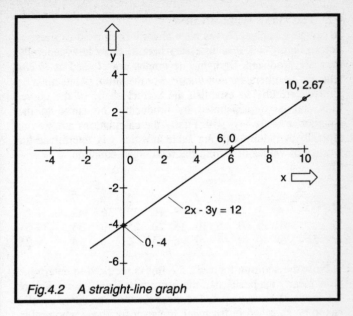

Fig.4.2   A straight-line graph

if $x = 0$, $y = -4$ if $y = 0$, $x = 6$.

Next comes the problem of choosing the extent of the graph
and from this the scales to be used. Suppose here that we wish
to examine what happens over the range of x from –4 to +10.
Suitable scales might be as in Figure 4.2 on which the straight-
line graph of $2x - 3y = 12$ is drawn.

It is possible to check the calculations by finding the value
of y for any other value of x or even by extending the line to a
further point, say at $x = 10$. In this case $20 - 3y = 12$ so that $y
= 8/3 = 2.67$. By extending the line on the graph as shown, it is
clear that at this point y is equal to 2.67 so confirming that the
line drawn is correct.

Straight-line graphs are therefore the simplest, and we have
already shown in Figure 3.1 how easily two such graphs may
be used to solve simultaneous equations.

4.2 The Many Types of Curve

Although graphical curves have already been used as illustration in Figure 3.3, it is necessary here to show how generally they are produced. Straight-line graphs are classed as *linear* whereas all others are *non-linear*. For the latter, points must be plotted carefully to establish the correct shape of the curve. This can be demonstrated by producing the curve to the equation $x^2 - 5x - y = 0$. Firstly the calculations are set out typically as in the following Table in which y is determined for a range of values of x from the rearranged equation, $y = x^2 - 5x$.

x	–2	–1	0	1	2	3	4	5	6	7	2.5
x^2	4	1	0	1	4	9	16	25	36	49	6.25
$5x$	–10	–5	0	5	10	15	20	25	30	35	12.5
$x^2 - 5x$	14	6	0	–4	–6	–6	–4	0	6	14	–6.25

Note the addition for $x = 2.5$ – this is required to determine more clearly the position of the curve at its lowest point. Figure 4.3 shows the curve plotted to these results. The curve usually has to be sketched in freehand, however for those who prefer, 'French curves' are available. These are plastic templates to help with drawing all kinds of curved lines.

A rising curve (sloping upwards to the right) is said to have a positive slope. A curve moving downwards to the right has a negative slope as shown. Between $x = 0$ and $x = 5$, y is negative hence the curve lies in quadrant 4 and where x is negative the curve lies in quadrant 2.

Solutions to the equation can now be read directly from the curve e.g. the values of x when $y = 4$ are shown to be 5.7 and –0.70. These results can be confirmed by 'completing the square' as shown in Section 3.2.3.

This is a case of a smooth curve following a particular mathematical formula. When certain experimental results are plotted however, things may not go so smoothly because observations may include some errors. It is then necessary to draw the curve as evenly as possible among the plotted points so that generally an equal number of results lies on each side of any small section of the curve, i.e. in a way an average is being taken.

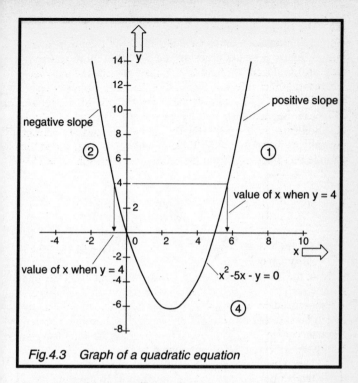

Fig.4.3   Graph of a quadratic equation

4.2.1 Straightening a Curve

Peculiarly enough certain curves can be plotted as straight lines. Take for example the general expression for a non-linear device such as shown in Figure 3.4. This is $i = kv^n$, showing that the current (i) varies not directly as the voltage (v) but at some power (n) of v instead. k and n vary with the material used in the device, when both are known, the curve for the device can be plotted. However this can be avoided by taking logarithms of both sides of the equation, i.e.

$$\log i = \log k + n \log v$$

the equation is now that of a straight line becuase no power index is involved.

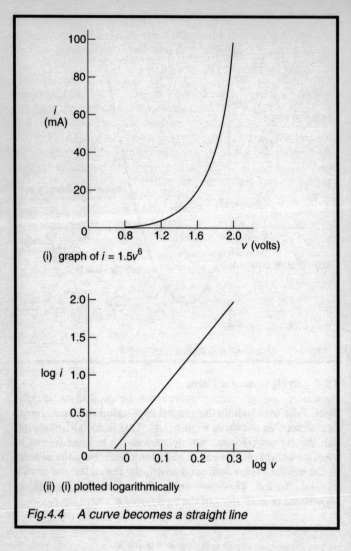

(i) graph of $i = 1.5v^6$

(ii) (i) plotted logarithmically

Fig.4.4   A curve becomes a straight line

From this, given various experimental corresponding values of i and v, it is possible to calculate the numerical values of k and n.

Consider a non-linear device conforming to the equation $i = kv^n$ and that experimentally the value of k has been found to be 1.5 and that of n to be 6. The equation now becomes

$$i = 1.5 v^6$$

where i is in milliamperes and v in volts.

At (i) in Figure 4.4 is shown plotted the normal curve and the non-linearity is immediately evident. Next we plot the curve in logarithmic units, i.e. log i v log v and this is shown in (ii) of the Figure, the 'curve' has now become a perfectly straight line and as we have already found, only two points need to be calculated to position the line exactly.

Many equations found in engineering are of this form and therefore are amenable to the above treatment. As a single example the pressure (p) and volume (v) of the gas in the cylinder of a steam or gas engine are connected in the form $p = kv^n$ which is recognized immediately as being of the required form. Most expressions which follow some kind of exponential law can be analysed in this way.

Incidentally, graph paper scaled logarithmically is available but it is suggested that using this type of graticule will only add to our woes.

4.2.2 Asymptotes

An asymptote is a line on a graph which continually approaches a given curve yet never actually meets it or as we prefer to say, meets it at infinity. As a demonstration we choose the equation $y = x - 1/x$ for which the graph for positive values of x is shown in Figure 4.5. For clarity the section of the curve for negative values of x has been omitted – it is in fact a mirror image of the curve shown and passes through $x = -1$, $y = 0$. The curve in the Figure passes through $x = 1$, $y = 0$.

When $x = 0$, y becomes infinitely large, hence one point of the asymptote is at $x = 0$. As x approaches infinity ($\rightarrow \infty$), y also approaches infinity, however from the Figure it is clear that when x is large, y is also from which it is evident that $y = x$ is the equation to the asymptote.

This is one particular example, it will be found that many curves approach infinity along a straight line as the Figure demonstrates.

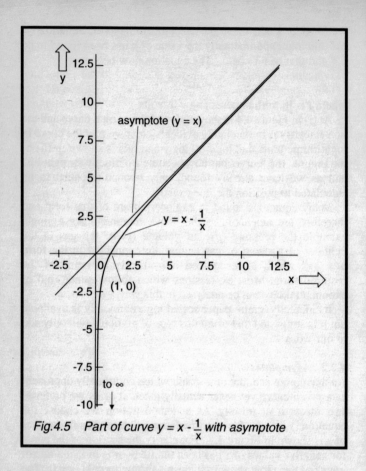

Fig.4.5   Part of curve $y = x - \frac{1}{x}$ with asymptote

4.2.3   Equations to Curves

With the experience we have now gained from the above three Sections, it is possible to appreciate the shape and usefulness of several different types of curve. Each has its own story to tell and in fact the equation to which it is drawn may usually be determined by observation. Figure 4.6 shows the curves to a selection of equations.

(1) Is of course the simplest. Whatever the value of x, y is equal

to a constant k, the result being a straight line parallel to the x axis. The equation is therefore $y = k$.

(2) Is again of straight lines, now not parallel to the x axis but at some angle or slope, m (an explanation of m is given on the Figure). If the line passes through $x = 0$ at $y = b$, the equation is $y = mx + b$. If it passes through $y = 0$ but at $x = a$, the equation becomes $y = m(x - a)$

(3) This is a more complicated straight-line graph passing through both $x = a, y = 0$ and also $x = 0, y = b$, this is the result of the equation

$$\frac{x}{a} + \frac{y}{b} = 1.$$

(4) If r is the radius of a circle, then the equation to the circle with its centre at the origin O is simply $x^2 + y^2 = r^2$ which follows from Pythagoras' theorem. Move the circle to any other point at $x = a, y = b$ and the equation becomes $(x - a)^2 + (y - b)^2 = r^2$. Proof of this follows in Section 5.3.1.

(5) The ellipse, briefly defined as a *regular oval*, has come to attention lately because certain satellite orbits are elliptical. Instead of a single radius as for a circle, it has two dimensions as shown, here labelled a and b and which are known as the semi-axes. With its centre at the origin O, the equation is of the general form

$$\frac{x^2}{a^2} + \frac{y^2}{b^2} = 1.$$

(6) This is the parabola which has also come to attention lately because it is the shape of many satellite antennas. The Figure shows a parabola with its vertex at the origin O and its own axis running along the x-axis. The equation is $y^2 = 4fx$ where the point f is known as the focus. In satellite transmission f is the point to which rays arriving parallel to the axis are reflected.

Note that none of the above contains asymptotes. However more complicated curves such as those of *hyperbolas* (see Sect. 5.5) are likely to include one or more.

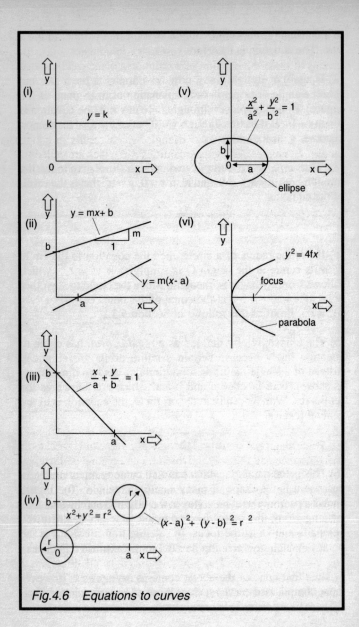

Fig.4.6 Equations to curves

4.2.4 Polar Coordinates

So far we have considered cartesian coordinates only. By means of these the position of a point on a plane can be stated. However we can also specify the position of a point (P) on a plane by means of its distance (r) from the fixed point O (the *origin* or *pole*) together with the angle the line OP makes with the reference axis Ox as shown in Figure 4.7. Here for demonstration is the familiar 3,4,5 triangle which results in a right angle. P is expressed by the quantities r, θ which are called the *polar coordinates* and in this particular case, relative to the line Ox, P is positioned at $5\angle36.9°$.

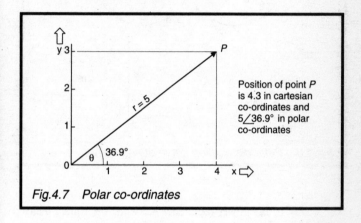

Position of point P is 4.3 in cartesian co-ordinates and $5\angle36.9°$ in polar co-ordinates

Fig.4.7   Polar co-ordinates

Polar diagrams are especially useful in the study of antenna performance and the way in which it can be done is illustrated by Figure 4.8. Such a power radiation diagram is drawn by plotting the power radiated versus the angle (θ), usually measured from the x-axis. The power radiated is represented by the length of the line from the polar diagram centre to the plotted point.

We imagine a single dipole antenna to be situated at the centre of the diagram. The power radiated in all directions is shown by the two loops. The concentric circles of the polar diagram are labelled with the estimated power radiated in the particular direction relative to the 0-180° line, for example at:

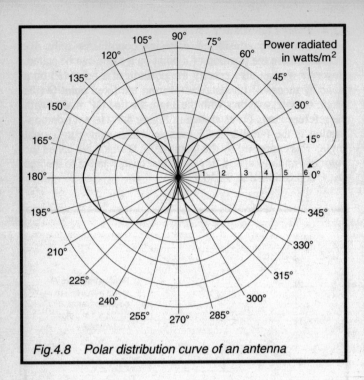

Fig.4.8   Polar distribution curve of an antenna

0° & 180°	the power radiated = 4.5 watts per square metre
30° & 150°	the power radiated = 3.65 watts per square metre
60° & 120°	the power radiated = 2.0 watts per square metre

and clearly the power radiated can be estimated for any direction. Note that the radiation is zero at 90° and 270° which is what would be expected from a dipole. The calculations involved here are not shown because they involve trigonometrical functions, the study of which is delayed until Chapter 6.

4.2.5   Gradient of a Graph

Gradient or degree of slope of a straight-line graph is easily defined as the ratio of the vertical distance between any two

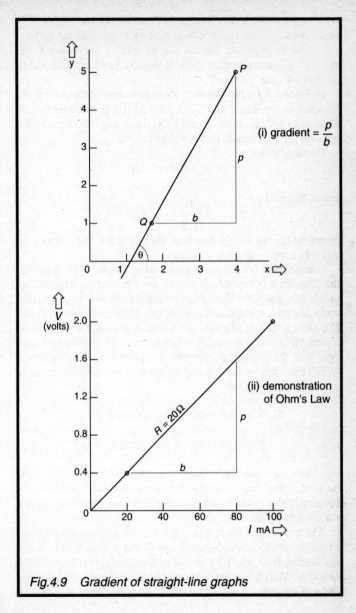

Fig.4.9   Gradient of straight-line graphs

points on the line to the horizontal distance between them. Any two points may be used because with a straight line the slope is the same throughout. This is not so with a curve hence the method of determining its slope is slightly more complicated as developed later.

In Figure 4.9 (i) is shown a straight-line graph and on it we take any two points P and Q. A vertical line is dropped from P to meet a horizontal line from Q. Let these two lines be labelled p and b (perpendicular and base) as shown.

On this drawing

$$p = 4, \quad b = 2.3$$

hence gradient

$$= \frac{4}{2.3} = 1.74$$

(from which we would find that the angle θ is 60° – more on this when we meet trigonometry).

Considering next a more practical example, it is clear that the linearity of Ohm's Law allows us to produce a straight-line graph for any particular value of resistance so that the agreement between voltage and current can immediately be read off. Consider a resistor of unknown value. Knowing the graph to be a straight line, it is normally only necessary to specify two voltages with the currents they produce to be able to draw the graph which can then be used for calculation of the resistance. As an example suppose that:

$$V = 2.0 \text{ volts}, \quad I = 100 \text{ mA}$$

also $\qquad V = 0.4 \text{ volts}, \quad I = \quad 20 \text{ mA}$

we can then draw the straight line as in Figure 4.9(ii). Note however that the second calculation is often unnecessary because when $V = 0$, I must be 0 in every case therefore any line must emanate from 0.

The gradient of the line is given by p/b, i.e. in volts required to produce one ampere of current (V/A) which in fact is the resistance. Here $p = 1.2$V, $b = 60$mA so that $R = p/b = 1.2$V/60 mA $= 1.2$V/0.06A $= 20\Omega$ hence it is clear that the resistance is indicated by the *gradient* of the *V/I* graph. This can easily be

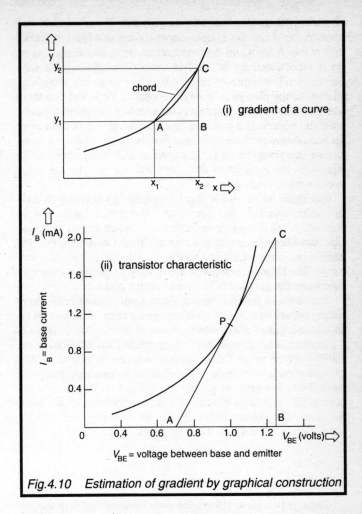

Fig.4.10   Estimation of gradient by graphical construction

proved by constructing the straight-line graphs for other values of resistance.

As mentioned earlier in this Section, determining the gradient of a curve graphically is a more complex procedure than that for a straight line simply because the gradient is continually changing around the curve. Accordingly the point on a curve at which the gradient is measured must be stated. Let us develop this from the simple curve shown in Figure 4.10(i). Two points A and C on the curve are at $x_1 y_1$ and $x_2 y_2$. $(y_2 - y_1)$ is represented by BC and is the net change in y for the change in x, here represented by AB. The change in y therefore relative to the change in x might appear to be at the constant rate BC/AB. However the rate is not constant because the characteristic is curved, a constant rate would imply a straight line between A and C. Such a straight line as in the Figure, i.e. one joining two points on an arc is known as a *chord* hence BC/AB represents the gradient of the chord AC, i.e. the rise (or fall) over a certain range of x.

If next the length of the chord is reduced by bringing x_1 and x_2 closer together, the curve and the chord become progressively less dissimilar and eventually when x_1 and x_2 coincide the chord becomes a *tangent* (from Latin, *tangere*, to touch), i.e. a line which just touches but does not intersect the curve. The tangent, being at a point only therefore accurately represents the gradient of the curve at that point.

The problem now is – how is the tangent constructed? Very simply indeed, it is drawn carefully with a ruler. An example is shown in Figure 4.10(ii) which shows an input characteristic of a transistor. The triangle ABC is completed for calculation of AB/BC which gives the resistance at point P. Generally the triangle should be as large as possible for accuracy of measurement. Note that here we are placing voltage on the x-axis with current on the y-axis which is the arrangement generally used for transistor characteristics. From the drawing, AB = 0.55 volts, BC = 2.0 mA, i.e. 0.002 amperes, hence

$$\text{resistance at P} = \frac{0.55 \text{ V}}{0.002 \text{ A}} = 275 \text{ ohms.}$$

There is of course always the possibility of slight inaccuracy with graphical methods. The result can also be obtained by calculation if the equation to the curve is known and in fact the calculated value is 273 ohms, a good correlation in this case.

4.2.6 Some Interesting Graphs
There are many different types of graph in which we are likely

to become involved in the study of electronics. We will find that exponential laws occur very frequently in physics and electronics hence this Section looks at just two examples from which we can gain a little more experience. Trigonometry also involves graphical illustration, this is delayed until Chapter 6.

(1) Graph of $y = 10^x$:

Calculation of the values of y for a range of values of x can without a calculator most easily be made by logarithms. Let us take a range for x from –1 to +1. Taking positive values first and remembering that the logarithm of 10 is 1, then for example, when $x = 0.5$, $10^{0.5}$ is obtained from the antilog of 0.5 which is 3.162 (try looking up the logarithm of 3.162, it is equal to 0.5). Again, when $x = 0.25$, $10^{0.25}$ from the antilog tables is 1.778 and so on for all the points required for positive values of x. Of course when $x = 0$, $y = 1$. For negative values, for example when $x = -0.25$ then $10^{-0.25} = 10^{-1} \times 10^{0.75}$, i.e $1/10 \times 5.623 = 0.5623$.

The scientific calculator makes light of this for in the last case as an example, the requirement is merely to enter 10 then –0.25 at the y^x button to give the answer above.

The graph is shown in Figure 4.11(i) and from it the value of 10^x can be read off with reasonable accuracy for any value of x within the range. As an example, at $x = 0.36$, the graph shows that $y = 2.3$ (by calculator, $y = 2.291$). Again at $x = -0.2$, $y = 0.6$ (by calculator, 0.631).

Clearly in this case especially, the graph is a useful and pictorial guide but it can never quite have the accuracy of calculation.

(2) Graph of $y = e^x$ and $y = e^{-x}$:

The use of e as the base of Natural (Napierian) logarithms is introduced in Section 2.5. Although in purely mathematical calculations common logarithms (to base 10) seem to be less complicated to use, when later we study Calculus it will be found that natural logarithms (to the base e) take over.

For our calculations tables of both e^x and e^{-x} may be used directly. If no such tables are available but common logarithms

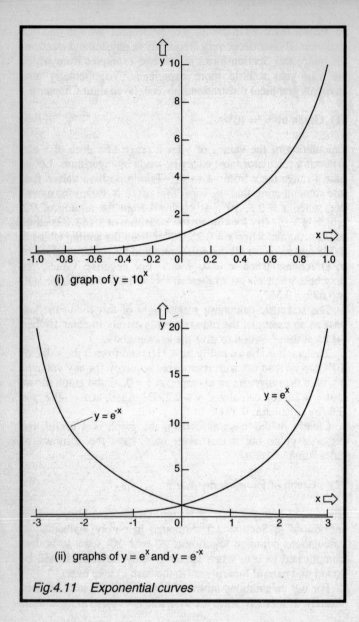

(i) graph of y = 10^x

(ii) graphs of y = e^x and y = e^{-x}

y = e^{-x}

y = e^x

Fig.4.11 Exponential curves

are, then because $e = 2.7183$,

$$\log_{10}e = 0.4343 \quad \text{and} \quad e = 10^{0.4343}$$

hence $$e^x = 10^{0.4343x}$$

As an example, when $x = 2$, $e^x = 10^{0.8686}$ which from antilog tables is equal to 7.389.

Again when $x = -2$,

$$e^x = 10^{-0.8686} = \frac{1}{10^{0.8686}} = 0.135.$$

The two graphs are shown in Figure 4.11. It is evident that both curves are positive for any value of x. For positive values of x, $e^x \rangle 1$ and $e^{-x} \langle 1$. Also it is evident that as x increases towards infinity, e^x does also whereas e^{-x} tends to zero.

Chapter 5

GEOMETRY

"Geometry" arises from the Greek, *geo*, earth and *metron*, measure, hence meaning "earth-measuring" which indicates its original purpose. In fact, as early as 1000–2000 BC earth measurement became important to the Egyptians who lost the boundaries of surrounding plots of land each time the Nile flooded. In those days they used ropes for measuring lengths and constructing angles. Certainly the pyramids also needed some applications of geometry. Much later in Greece geometrical theorems began to be deduced, for example it was Thales of Miletus who in the 600's BC discovered that the angle within a semicircle is a right angle.

Three centuries later, the "father of geometry", *Euclid* published his 'Elements of Geometry' which is the basis of classical geometry, even today. Euclid's name is now invariably linked with geometry and through it he has become one of the most famous of mathematicians.

The definition of geometry as the science of measurement of the earth is both out of date and inadequate, in a way we ourselves might define it as a branch of mathematics dealing with lines and spaces and their relationship. There is *plane* geometry which is two-dimensional only (angles, squares, circles, etc.) and also *solid* geometry for spheres, cubes and other three-dimensional bodies.

5.1 The Basic Concepts

It may be appropriate to brush up on some definitions first. There is a fundamental idea in geometry which is that of *ratio* because every measurement involves comparison, in other words all measurements are relative. Accordingly we have to decide on standards which are acceptable to everyone. Take the unit of length, the metre as an example. The standard has changed with time from the original (one ten millionth of the distance from the North Pole to the Equator, via Paris) to the distance between two marks on a special metal bar (kept in a vault for safety). Subsequently it was defined in terms of the wavelength of a certain radiation and now finally as the length of the path travelled in a vacuum by light during 1 / 299 792 458 seconds (which also reminds us that light travels in a vacuum at 2.997 925 metres per second).

5.1.1 The Constant π

This particular constant which we meet so often is simply the ratio of the circumference to the diameter of a circle {see Fig.5.2 (ix)}. In the 3rd century BC Archimedes realized its importance and he did his best to calculate the value. Unfortunately the actual value is never-ending and he had not the facilities we enjoy today so his efforts, although subsequently in use for a long time, were hardly what we now would consider as accurate. By the year 1610, π had been calculated to 35 decimal places whereas more recently we have reached 100 000 decimal places. Generally however we ourselves are satisfied with just a few, e.g. $\pi \approx 3.141\ 592\ 654$ as shown on many calculators or perhaps more usefully as 3.142, but note the ever present $\approx$, i.e. the *approximately equals* sign. A few useful figures based on π are:

$$\pi \approx 3.14159 \quad 1/\pi \approx 0.31831 \quad \sqrt{\pi} \approx 1.77245$$

$$\pi^2 \approx 9.869\ 60 \quad \log \pi \approx 0.497\ 1$$

As fractions: $\dfrac{22}{7}$ (= 3.142 86) $\dfrac{355}{113}$ (= 3.141 592 92)

– this last fraction is sufficiently accurate for most purposes.

5.1.2 Angles

Angles arise out of the relationship of lines to one another. An angle can be defined simply as the space between two lines in contact. At the point where the lines meet is the *vertex* generally marked O on a diagram.

Appendix 2 shows that in the SI, angles are measured in *radians*, usually abbreviated to *rad*. A radian is the angle at the centre of a circle subtended by an arc of length equal to the radius. This is shown in Figure 5.1 (i) and it is evident that:

92

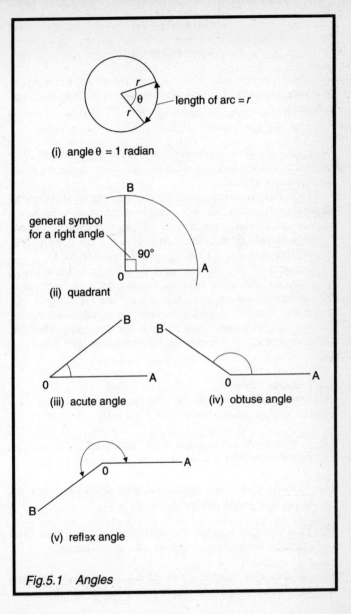

(i) angle θ = 1 radian

general symbol for a right angle

90°

(ii) quadrant

(iii) acute angle

(iv) obtuse angle

(v) reflex angle

Fig.5.1 Angles

$$\theta \text{ radians} = \frac{\text{length of arc } (s)}{\text{circle radius } (r)}$$

and this is independent of the size of the circle. Rearranging gives another useful relationship from which arc lengths can be calculated:

$$s = \theta \times r.$$

Now since the circumference of any circle is of a length $2\pi \times$ the radius, it is evident that, from the definition above, there are 2π radians in a circle.

The radian has many uses in technology but we still cling to degrees in everyday life. Accordingly whereas we work to 2π radians to the circle, there are also 360 degrees with the symbol °, hence 2π rads are equivalent to 360°, i.e. 1 rad is equivalent to $360/2\pi$ degrees = 57.296°, generally taken as 57.3°.

A quarter of the circumference of a circle is known as a *quadrant* and the angle between the two radii enclosing it is 90°, otherwise known as a *right angle* {see Fig. 5.1(ii)}. An angle less than 90° is said to be *acute* as is shown on Figure 5.1(iii). Angles greater than 90° but not exceeding 180° are labelled *obtuse* (iv) whereas angles exceeding 180° are *reflex* (v).

5.1.3 Plane Figures
Next we consider some of the well-known plane figures considered in classical geometry – see Figure 5.2.

(1) A triangle has 3 straight sides. When all sides and all angles are equal, it is said to be an *equilateral* triangle.

(2) Two triangles which coincide exactly when superimposed are said to be *congruent*.

(3) Two triangles which are of different sizes but have their corresponding angles equal are said to be *similar*.

(4) An *isosceles* triangle (from Greek *isos*, equal) has two equal sides. The angles opposite these sides are also equal.

94

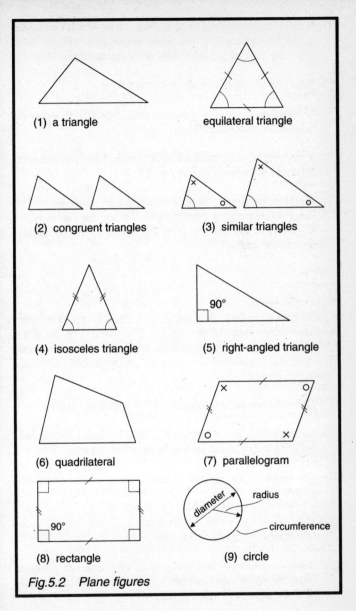

(1) a triangle

equilateral triangle

(2) congruent triangles

(3) similar triangles

(4) isosceles triangle

(5) right-angled triangle

90°

(6) quadrilateral

(7) parallelogram

(8) rectangle

90°

(9) circle

diameter

radius

circumference

Fig.5.2   Plane figures

(5) A *right-angled* triangle is any triangle in which one angle is a right angle (90°). The three angles of a triangle total 180°, the sum of the other two angles is therefore 90°.

(6) A *quadrilateral* is any plane 4-sided figure.

(7) A *parallelogram* is a 4-sided plane figure with opposite sides equal and parallel.

(8) A *rectangle* is a parallelogram with four right-angles. Adjacent sides need not be equal.

(9) The line forming a circle is called the *circumference*. The straight line passing from side to side via the centre is the *diameter*. A straight line from the centre to the circumference is the *radius*.

5.1.4 Geometric Solids

A solid is an object which occupies space and is separated from the surrounding space by its surface. Compared with the plane figures in the above Section, it does not lie in a plane but occupies a third dimension. Some easily recognizable solids are shown in Figure 5.3.

(1) The *cube* has six equal faces, all of which are squares.

(2) A *rectangular parallelepiped* (a solid bounded by parallelograms) is as shown, all the faces are rectangles.

(3) The faces of an *oblique parallelepiped* are all parallelograms.

(4) The *triangular pyramid* shown has 3 equal triangular faces constructed on a triangular base.

(5) Shows a *frustrum* (the lower part of a cone or pyramid when the upper part has been sliced off parallel to the base) of a *pentagonal* (5 sides) pyramid.

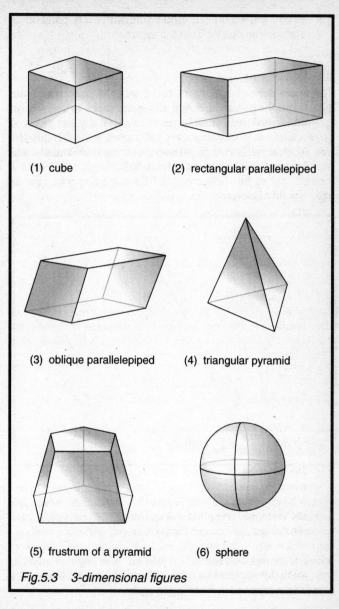

(1) cube

(2) rectangular parallelepiped

(3) oblique parallelepiped

(4) triangular pyramid

(5) frustrum of a pyramid

(6) sphere

Fig.5.3   3-dimensional figures

(6) Shows a *sphere*, i.e. a solid figure with every point on its surface equidistant from the centre.

5.2 Parallel Lines

These are defined simply as being straight lines which are continuously equidistant, hence they never meet. In contrast we have all learned that parallel lines meet at infinity, but this is of no practical use to us whatsoever. Of interest is the fact that any pair of straight lines *not* parallel must meet eventually and furthermore three non-parallel lines will intersect and form a triangle and so on. Hence parallel lines are a special case as even Euclid discovered.

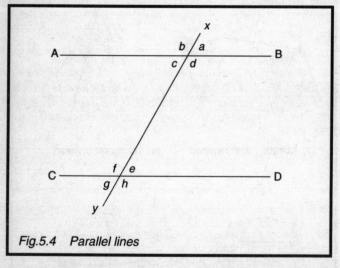

Fig.5.4 Parallel lines

If a straight line cuts a system of lines, it is known as a *transversal* hence the line *xy* in Figure 5.4 is one and when this happens there are several important relationships which arise between the angles formed. Firstly however there is a relationship which affects all straight lines which intersect such as *xy* where it crosses AB (or CD). There are four angles formed at the crossing point marked in the Figure *a*, *b*, *c*, *d*. Here angles *a* and *c* are equal, also *b* and *d* are equal.

For the parallel lines:

(1) The *corresponding* angles such as a and e are equal, therefore from the relationship mentioned above, c and g are also equal simply because $a = c$ and $e = g$. The remaining angles may be considered similarly.

(2) From (1) it follows that the *alternate* angles are equal, e.g. $c = e$. This follows because if $a = e$ and $a = c$, then $c = e$.

(3) The interior opposite angles, i.e. d and e, also c and f are supplementary (i.e. the pair add up to $180°$). This follows because if, for example d and c are supplementary and $c = e$, then d and e are supplementary.

5.3 Circles

We have already met the circle briefly as a plane figure in Section 5.1.3. It is of interest that a circle encloses a greater area than any other plane figure having the same perimeter. Other terms relating to circles are now appropriate, see Figure 5.5.

(1) On both sides of a diameter are *semicircles*.

(2) An *arc* is part of the circumference of a circle (or any other curve).

(3) A *sector* is the area enclosed between two radii of a circle.

(4) A *chord* is a straight line joining the ends of an arc.

(5) A *tangent* is a straight line which just touches but does not intersect a circle, drawn from a point outside the circle.

(6) A *segment* is that part of a circle enclosed between an arc and a chord. The two segments formed are classified as major and minor as shown.

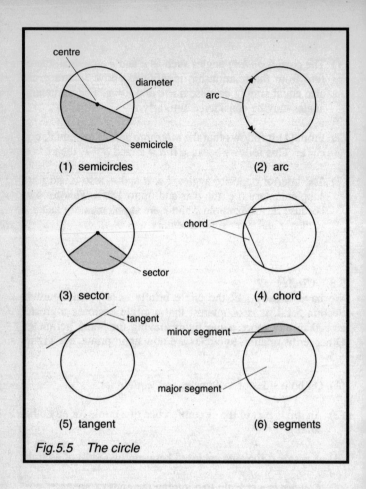

centre

diameter

arc

semicircle

(1) semicircles

(2) arc

chord

sector

(3) sector

(4) chord

tangent

minor segment

major segment

(5) tangent

(6) segments

Fig.5.5 The circle

5.3.1 The Equations to a Circle

In determining the equation to any given circle, its position must be known and generally this is relative to the two normal axes which almost invariably are at right angles. These two axes are shown in Figure 5.6(i) and with the point O (the origin) as the centre, a circle is drawn. Take any point P on the circle and join OP. Let the coordinates of P be x and y, then:

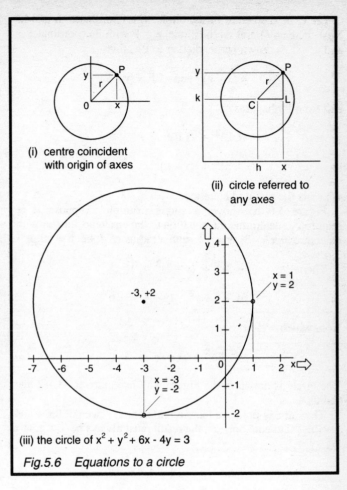

(i) centre coincident with origin of axes

(ii) circle referred to any axes

(iii) the circle of $x^2 + y^2 + 6x - 4y = 3$

Fig.5.6   Equations to a circle

$$x^2 + y^2 = r^2$$

– this is therefore the general equation to a circle the centre of which coincides with the origin of the two axes.

Going one step further let us next develop the equation to a circle, the centre of which does not coincide with the origin of the axes, see Figure 5.6(ii).

101

Let C be the centre of the circle with coordinates h and k. Next, take any point on the circle, e.g. P with its coordinates x and y. CL is drawn perpendicular to Px, then

$$CL = (x - h) \quad \text{and} \quad LP = (y - k)$$

and from Pythagoras:

$$(CL)^2 + (LP)^2 = r^2$$

i.e.
$$(x - h)^2 + (y - k)^2 = r^2 \qquad ....(1)$$

which is the required equation.

Figure 5.6(iii) shows a single example. Suppose it is required to determine the equation to the circle positioned with its centre at $x = -3$, $y = +2$ with a radius of 4, i.e. h = -3, k = 2, $r = 4$.

Then:
$$(x + 3)^2 + (y - 2)^2 = 16$$

∴
$$x^2 + 6x + 9 + y^2 - 4y + 4 = 16$$

from which:

$$x^2 + y^2 + 6x - 4y = 3 \qquad ....(2)$$

The circle is drawn in the Figure with its centre at -3, $+2$ and radius 4.

Then at any point on the circumference, if we put the x and y values into equation (2), the result must always be 3, e.g. at $x = 1$, $y = 2$:

$$x^2 + y^2 + 6x - 4y = 1 + 4 + 6 - 8 = 3.$$

Also at $x = -3$, $y = -2$:

$$x^2 + y^2 + 6x - 4y = 9 + 4 - 18 + 8 = 3$$

proving that we now have a circle obeying equation (1).

5.4 Areas and Volumes

Some of the plane and 3-dimensional figures are illustrated in Figures 5.2 and 5.3. Here we examine them further but note that these figures are in a way, neat and tidy. Measuring for example a large plot of land requires extra help such as that of a *theodolite* which is a surveying instrument for measuring both horizontal and vertical angles to distant points. From these distances can be calculated, but let us not forget the simple tape measure.

5.4.1 Areas

We take perhaps the easiest one first, the area of a rectangle which as shown in Figure 5.7 at (1) is simply length, $l \times$ height, h, both of which must be in the same units, e.g. if l is in metres, h must be also so that their product (the area) will be in square metres. The diagonal AC clearly cuts the figure into two equal areas hence the area of the figure in (2) is $1/2\, l \times h$ which is the area of a right-angled triangle. When the triangle does not contain a right angle, the rule still applies provided that h is the perpendicular height as shown in (3).

The area of a square follows for if l and h are equal, then the area is equal to l^2 or h^2. A quadrilateral, i.e. a plane 4-sided figure, no sides parallel or equal can be divided into two triangles, the area of the quadrilateral then being the sum of the areas of the triangles.

(4) shows that, as with the rectangle, a parallelogram (opposite sides equal and parallel) is a rectilinear (straight lines) figure which again can be considered as two triangles as shown. Its area is obviously twice that of the triangle which is $(l \times h)/2 \times 2$, i.e. $l \times h$. Note also that diagonally opposite angles are equal, e.g. $\angle\,ADC = \angle\,ABC$ and that the diagonals bisect each other, e.g. $AE = EC$.

A *rhombus* is a special form of parallelogram in which all sides are equal and the diagonals are at right angles to each other.

The *trapezium* in (5) in which l_1 and l_2 are parallel is again formed by two triangles, e.g. by ABC and ACD. From this it is evident that the area of ABCD is $\frac{1}{2}l_1 h + \frac{1}{2}l_2 h$, i.e. $\frac{1}{2}(l_1 + l_2)$.

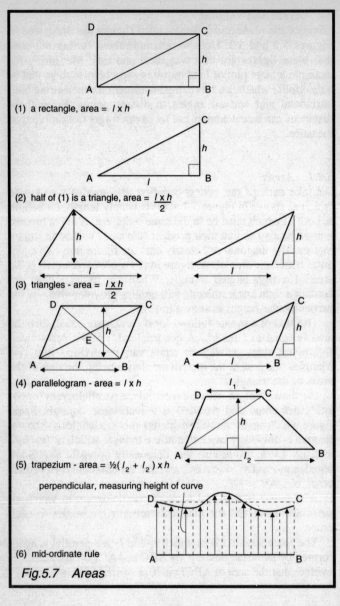

(1) a rectangle, area = $l \times h$

(2) half of (1) is a triangle, area = $\dfrac{l \times h}{2}$

(3) triangles - area = $\dfrac{l \times h}{2}$

(4) parallelogram - area = $l \times h$

(5) trapezium - area = $\frac{1}{2}(l_1 + l_2) \times h$

perpendicular, measuring height of curve

(6) mid-ordinate rule

Fig.5.7   Areas

104

5.4.2 Areas of Irregular Figures

Several methods exist for calculation of the area under a curve, that is between the curve and the axis of x or any other base line, the degree of accuracy usually being a function of the complexity of the method. When an equation to the curve exists the answer is easily obtained by calculus, however this cannot cater for irregularities. When these exist a reasonably accurate result can be obtained by use of the *mid-ordinate rule*.

Consider the curve shown in Figure 5.7 at (6). The principle is simply that if h is the mean ordinate of the irregular figure ABCD, then the area of the figure is given by $h \times$ AB. To find the mean ordinate the base is evenly divided by the dotted lines as shown and at the mid points perpendiculars are drawn. The sum of all perpendiculars divided by their number is the mean ordinate. Clearly the accuracy of the result is increased as the number of ordinates increases.

The method is not as time-consuming as it may at first seem for the sum of the ordinates is obtained with least effort by using the edge of a sheet of paper, marking off a length equal to that of the first ordinate and at the end of this, marking off the length of the second ordinate and so on.

5.4.3 Volumes and Surface Areas

A *prism* is a 3-dimensional figure with its two ends similar, equal and parallel. It has a constant cross-sectional area and shape throughout its length. There are many solid figures within this category, here we consider two of them, see Figure 5.8 (1) and (2). The volumes of all prisms are given by multiplying the cross-sectional area of the base by the height. Surface areas are totalled from twice the area of one end plus the area of the remaining surface.

(1)   the *rectangular* prism. The cross-sectional area is $b \times l$, the length or height is h. The volume is therefore $b\,l\,h$.

Surface area of the two ends $= 2\,bl$
Surface area of the sides $= 2\,(bh + lh) = 2h\,(b + l)$
$\therefore$ total surface area $= 2\,\{bl + h(b + l)\}$

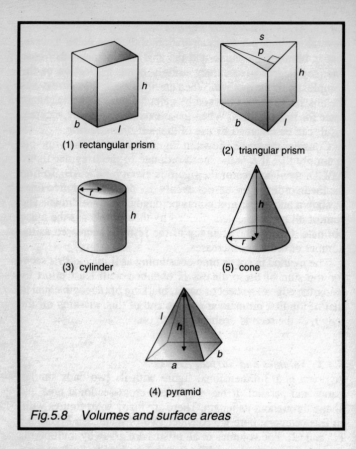

(1) rectangular prism

(2) triangular prism

(3) cylinder

(5) cone

(4) pyramid

Fig.5.8 Volumes and surface areas

(2) the *triangular* prism. The cross-sectional area is $\dfrac{l \times p}{2}$, length is h,

$$\therefore \qquad \text{volume} = \dfrac{lph}{2}$$

Surface area of the two ends $= 2 \times \dfrac{lp}{2} = lp$

Surface area of the three sides $= bh + lh + sh = h(b + l + s)$

106

$\therefore$ total surface area $= lp + h(b + l + s)$.

(3)   a circular *cylinder* follows the same rules as for prisms, here the cross-sectional area of the base $= \pi r^2$, the height is h, hence the volume is $\pi r^2 h$ {see (3) of the Figure}.

Surface area of the two ends	$= 2\pi r^2$
Area of the curved surface	$= 2\pi r \times h$
$\therefore$ total surface area	$= 2\pi r (r + h)$.

(4)   a *pyramid* is not a prism, accordingly the general formula changes. In (4) of the Figure note that h is now the height of the pyramid, not the measurement along its sloping side (which we now mark l).

If we imagine a cube with its centre point joined by a line to each of the 8 corners, then a pyramid will be formed on each of the 6 faces, the apexes of all the pyramids meeting at the centre. Accordingly the volume of each pyramid will be one sixth of that of the cube. Now if each side of the cube is labelled a then the height of each pyramid is $a/2$.

The volume of the cube $= a^3$, hence the volume of one pyramid is $\frac{1}{6} a^3$ which can be rewritten as

$$\frac{1}{3} a^2 \times \frac{a}{2}$$

so that:

Volume of pyramid $= \frac{1}{3}$ area of base $\times$ height,

i.e. $\frac{1}{3} abh$.

It is easy to imagine how the surface area is calculated because as with the pyramid shown, it is equal to the area of the base plus the total surface area of the sloping faces.

(5)   the *cone* has many similarities to the pyramid. In the Figure one is sketched of vertical height h, slant length l and base radius r.

Then volume of cone $= \frac{1}{3}$ area of base $\times$ height $= \frac{1}{3} \pi r^2 h$.

The curved surface area $= \pi r \times l$ hence the total surface area $= \pi r l + \pi r^2 = \pi r (l + r)$.

(6) for a *sphere* of radius r it can be shown that the volume is given by $\frac{4}{3}\pi r^3$ and the surface area by $4\pi r^2$. (These formulae are developed by integral calculus which for us comes later).

Volumes and surface areas of other more complex solids can usually be calculated based on the principles developed above.

5.5 Conic Sections

It is now necessary to expand on geometric curves which involve a feature known as *eccentricity*. This may be defined as "deviating from a circle" and within this class are the ellipse, parabola and hyperbola. They are known as *conic sections* because each is revealed when a cone is sliced in a certain way. Many years ago the Greek mathematician Apollonius discovered that when a cone is sliced at different angles the surface shapes varied and we now have them labelled as shown in Figure 5.9(i). Although these curves are important in the study of electronics, they are also everywhere in astronomy because any planet or comet must follow one of them. Many orbits of the planets are almost true circles but those of most comets are highly elliptical, others as shown in (ii) of the Figure are parabolic or hyperbolic, they travel round the sun once only, never to return.

Let us first consider the terms used in conjunction with conic sections:

A *conic section* is the locus of a point which moves so that its distance from a fixed point (the *focus*) is always in a constant ratio (the *eccentricity*) to its perpendicular distance from a fixed straight line (the *directrix*). The eccentricity is generally denoted by e.

when the eccentricity $e = 1$, the conic section is a parabola

when the eccentricity $e < 1$, the conic section is an ellipse

when the eccentricity $e > 1$, the conic section is a hyperbola {see Fig. 5.9(ii)}

We consider the parabola first, recalling that $e = 1$.

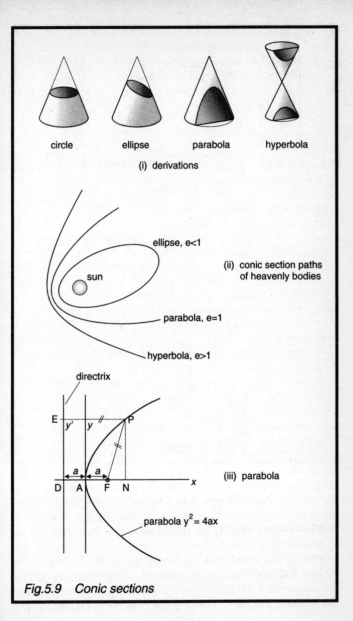

circle   ellipse   parabola   hyperbola

(i) derivations

ellipse, e<1

sun

parabola, e=1

hyperbola, e>1

(ii) conic section paths
of heavenly bodies

directrix

E   P

y'   y   //

D   A   F   N   x

a   a   //

(iii) parabola

parabola $y^2 = 4ax$

Fig.5.9   Conic sections

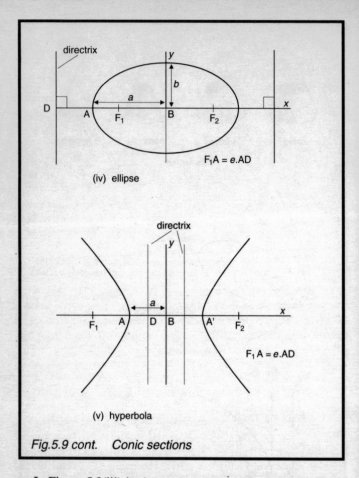

directrix

a

b

D

A

F_1

B

F_2

x

y

$F_1A = e.AD$

(iv) ellipse

directrix

y

a

F_1

A

D

B

A'

F_2

x

$F_1 A = e.AD$

(v) hyperbola

Fig.5.9 cont.   Conic sections

In Figure 5.9(iii) is shown the *vertex* of a parabola (at 0 on the *y*-axis). The directrix and focus are indicated and for any point P on the curve the distances to the directrix and to the focus are equal (this is what makes the eccentricity equal to 1).

In this Figure, let the focus, F as shown be on the axis of *x* and let the directrix be also as shown, perpendicular to D*x*. A is a point half-way between D and F and is therefore a point on the curve since AF/DA = 1 (the eccentricity). Let us represent the distance DA by *a*. Take a point P on the curve and drop a perpendicular PN onto the x axis. Then:

$$FN = DN - DF = DN - 2a$$

and if DN is represented by x, then $FN = x - 2a$.

Also since both PF and PE are equal to x and since $(PF)^2 = (PN)^2 + (FN)^2$, by here considering the directrix as the y' axis:

$$x^2 = y'^2 + (x - 2a)^2$$

hence $$y'^2 = 4a(x - a).$$

Alternatively we can shift the y-axis to the point A as shown, then $x - a$ becomes simply x and the equation to the parabola is now the general one:

$$y^2 = 4ax.$$

It is evident that for every positive value for x, by taking the square root, y must have two equal and opposite values. Also x and y are at zero together. Note especially that as x increases, so does y, hence finally when $x = \infty$, y does also, the parabola is therefore not a closed figure, this is illustrated in Figure 5.9(ii).

If x is negative, y is equal to the square root of a negative quantity hence the corresponding values of y are imaginary. This does not affect us here and imaginary quantities are explained in depth in Chapter 8.

For an *ellipse* the eccentricity is less than 1 as indicated in Figure 5.9(ii). It is in fact a closed figure with two foci as marked F_1 and F_2 in (iv) of the Figure, positioned on the x-axis so that, for example, $F_1A = e.AD$. The proof of the equation is reasonably straightforward and leads to the conclusion that for an ellipse:

$$\frac{x^2}{a^2} + \frac{y^2}{b^2} = 1$$

where a and b are the semi-axes as shown.

The x-axis is called the major axis, the y-axis is the minor.

The *hyperbola* as shown in Figure 5.9(v) is, as with the parabola, not a closed figure but now one with an eccentricity greater than 1. Because of this there are two separate sections of the curve as shown with the two foci F_1 and F_2 positioned on the x-axis so that $F_1A = e.AD$.

Let a represent the length AB (or A'B). Compared with the ellipse the proof is less straightforward and leads to the general equation:

$$\frac{x^2}{a^2} - \frac{y^2}{b^2} = 1 \qquad \text{where } b^2 = a^2 (e^2 - 1).$$

It is of interest that in (v) of the Figure, when e is large, say 10 or more, the shape of the hyperbola approaches that of a vertical straight line. As e is reduced towards 1 so the curvature increases and of course as we see above, at $e = 1$, it has changed into a parabola.

Chapter 6

TRIGONOMETRY

In this Chapter we are dealing with the study and application of the relationships involving the sides and angles of triangles. The rather complicated title has arrived here from the Greek and Latin, *tri* = 3, *gono* = cornered and *metry* = measure, clearly confirming that the subject is mainly about triangles.

We have already considered the relationship between degrees and radians in Section 5.1.2, generally however in trigonometry the degree is used in preference. As a reminder one degree is 1/360 th of a complete revolution. We take a circle and divide it up into its 4 quadrants, each of 90° as in Figure 6.1. Take any point P on the circumference of the circle, join PO and let this be marked *h*. Drop a perpendicular from P onto ON and label the triangle so formed, *hypotenuse*, *h*, *perpendicular*, *p* and *base*, *b*. Note that the triangle ONP is right-angled at N and that the hypotenuse is always longer than either of the other two sides. We see that as either of the angles θ and α change, then the sides must change in length. This in fact is what sine and cosine tables do, they tell us how the ratios between the perpendicular and the base relative to the hypotenuse change for any angle up to 90°.

For our sakes some very industrious people have calculated the ratios between pairs of sides (for any angle up to 90°) and the results are published in *Natural* sine (Latin, *sinus*, a curve), usually abbreviated to *sin*, cosine (*cos*) and tangent (*tan*) tables. They can also be obtained directly from a scientific calculator.

The sine of the angle θ is then defined as the ratio NP/OP, or using our labelling, *p/h* (perpendicular over hypotenuse). When P lies above the *x*-axis (quadrants 1 and 2), *p* is positive, therefore sin θ is positive. Conversely when P lies below the *x*-axis (quadrants 3 and 4), sin θ is negative.

Similarly the cosine of ∠θ is defined as the ratio ON/OP, i.e. *b/h* (base over hypotenuse). When P lies to the left of the *y*-axis (quadrants 2 and 3), *x* is negative hence cos θ is negative.

The tangent of ∠θ is then the ratio NP/ON, i.e. *p/b* (perpendicular over base).

113

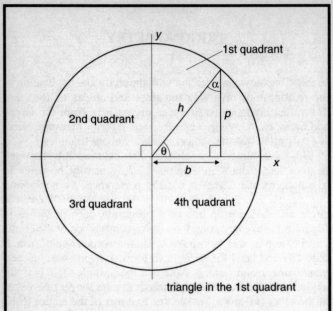

triangle in the 1st quadrant

Fig.6.1   Quadrants and trigonometric labelling

Now $\sin \theta = p/h, \ \cos \theta = b/h$

$\therefore$ $$\frac{\sin \theta}{\cos \theta} = \frac{p}{h} \times \frac{h}{b} = \frac{p}{b}$$

which is equal to tan θ,

hence $$\tan \theta = \frac{\sin \theta}{\cos \theta} \ .$$

We can now find whether the tangent is positive or negative in each of the 4 quadrants:

1st quadrant	sin +, cos +,	therefore tan is +
2nd quadrant	sin +, cos –,	therefore tan is –
3rd quadrant	sin –, cos –,	therefore tan is +
4th quadrant	sin –, cos +,	therefore tan is –

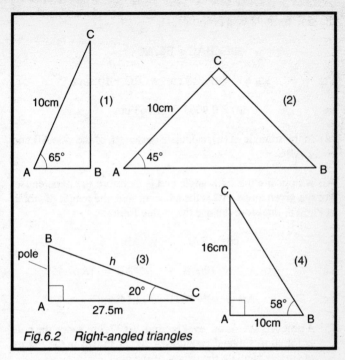

Fig.6.2   Right-angled triangles

For another way of remembering the ratios (and it is important to remember them!) we recall that h is the side opposite the
right angle, b is the side *adjacent* to the angle (θ) and p is the
side *opposite* the angle (θ). Then:

$$\sin \theta = \frac{\text{opposite}}{\text{hypotenuse}} \quad \cos \theta = \frac{\text{adjacent}}{\text{hypotenuse}} \quad \tan \theta = \frac{\text{opposite}}{\text{adjacent}} .$$

Here are a few examples, all concerned with right-angled
triangles – see Figure 6.2:

(1) In the triangle in (i), AC = 10 cm and $\angle$ BAC = 65°.
    What is the length of BC?

The side AC is opposite the right angle, it is therefore the
hypotenuse. BC is the side opposite the given angle, therefore

the sine formula is appropriate, i.e.

$$\sin \angle BAC = BC/AC$$

i.e. $\sin 65° = BC/10$ cm $\therefore$ BC $= 10 \sin 65°$

i.e. $10 \times 0.9063 = 9.063$ cm.

(2) In the triangle in (ii), calculate the length of the side AB and ∠ABC.

AB is opposite the right-angle and is therefore the hypotenuse. For the given angle, AC is the adjacent side, the length of which is known, therefore we use the cosine formula:

$$\cos \angle BAC = AC/AB$$

i.e. $\cos 45° = 10/AB$ $\therefore$ AB $= 10/\cos 45°$

i.e   AB $= 10/0.7071 = 14.14$ cm.

(3) A pole AB stands on level ground. At 27.5 m away, the pole is found to subtend an angle of 20° as shown in the Figure at (iii). Calculate the height of the pole.

$$\tan 20° = AB/AC = AB/27.5$$

$\therefore$ AB $= 27.5 \tan 20° = 27.5 \times 0.3640 = 10$ metres.

(4) To draw an angle of e.g. 58° using a ruler only. If we set up on squared paper AB and AC at right-angles in the ratio AC/AB of tan 58° (= 1.6 approx.), then completion of the triangle gives the angle required.

draw AB, say 10 cm and AC $10 \times 1.6 = 16$ cm,

then   ∠ABC $= 58°$.

Using this example we can now see how sin, cos or tan tables are used in reverse, i.e. to find the angle when given its trigonometrical function. As an example, for $\theta = 50°$, sin θ = 0.7660. This can alternatively be expressed as

$$\sin^{-1} 0.7660 = 50°$$

or as $$\text{arc sin } 0.7660 = 50°$$

thus $\sin^{-1}x$ (or arc sin x) is the angle the sine of which is x; also $\cos^{-1}x$ (or arc cos x) is the angle the cosine of which is x; and $\tan^{-1}x$ (or arc tan x) is the angle the tangent of which is x.

We can now rearrange the last example to demonstrate this. In (iv) of the Figure, calculate

$$\angle ABC \text{ when } AB = 10 \text{ cm, } AC = 16 \text{ cm.}$$

$$\tan \angle ABC = 16/10 = 1.6 \quad \therefore \quad \angle ABC = \tan^{-1} 1.6 = 58°.$$

The last calculation might also be written

$$\angle ABC = \text{arc tan } 1.6 = 58°.$$

6.1 Angles Exceeding 90°

When the radius OP in Figure 6.1 moves out of the 1st quadrant, the angle θ has a value greater than 90°, extending in the 2nd quadrant up to 180°, in the 3rd from 180 – 270° and in the 4th from 270 – 360°. As OP sweeps through each quadrant however it is clear that the right-angled triangles it forms repeat for each quadrant. Now in Figure 6.3 it is evident that considering OP_1 in the position shown, i.e. at $\theta°$ to the *reference* axis, this is equivalent to its being from the x^1 axis by (180 – θ)°. Accordingly if θ represents any angle through which the radius has turned, for the 2nd quadrant therefore we use (180 – θ)° in the normal (0 – 90)° trigonometrical tables.

Similarly for the 3rd quadrant use (θ – 180)° and for the 4th quadrant (360 – θ)° as shown in the Figure.

As an example, what is the value of cos 220°? 220° is in the 3rd quadrant therefore we look up (220 – 180)° in the normal tables which give for cos 40°, 0.7660. This is not yet complete

117

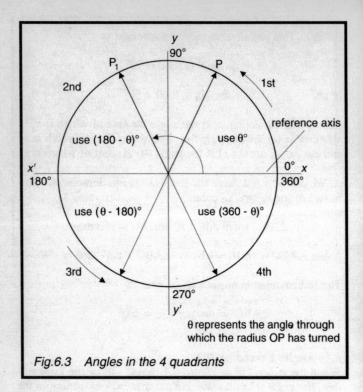

P₁

2nd

use (180 - θ)°

x'
180°

use (θ - 180)°

3rd

y
90°

P

1st

reference axis

use θ°

0° x
360°

use (360 - θ)°

4th

270°
y'

θ represents the angle through
which the radius OP has turned

Fig.6.3   Angles in the 4 quadrants

however because we have not yet checked for the sign. From
the tables for tangent at the beginning of this Chapter we find
that cos is negative in the 3rd quadrant, hence the correct
answer is –0.7660. (Note that a scientific calculator even puts
the sign in for us).

For sin 300° which is in the 4th quadrant, sin 60° is appropriate and again is negative, i.e. –0.8660.

6.2 Ratios For Some Particular Angles
There are some angles which present themselves quite frequently, mainly 30, 45 and 60 degrees. For 30 and 60 a good
idea is to picture or draw an equilateral triangle (all sides equal)
with sides of 2 units. A perpendicular divides the base into two

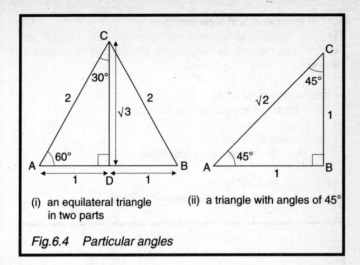

(i) an equilateral triangle in two parts

(ii) a triangle with angles of 45°

Fig.6.4   Particular angles

equal parts as shown in Figure 6.4(i). Now because for example, ACD is a right-angled triangle, then by Pythagoras:

$$\text{the length CD} = \sqrt{(2^2 - 1^2)} = \sqrt{3}$$

Hence $\sin 60° = \dfrac{\sqrt{3}}{2}$, $\cos 60° = \dfrac{1}{2}$, $\tan 60° = \sqrt{3}$.

Also $\sin 30° = \dfrac{1}{2}$, $\cos 30° = \dfrac{\sqrt{3}}{2}$, $\tan 30° = \dfrac{1}{\sqrt{3}}$.

For an angle of 45° we need a triangle in which the side AB is equal to the side BC as shown in Figure 6.4(ii). The angles at A and C are then both equal to 45°. Let the sides AB and BC be both equal to 1. Then by Pythagoras, AC = $\sqrt{2}$.

Hence $\sin 45° = \dfrac{1}{\sqrt{2}}$, $\cos 45° = \dfrac{1}{\sqrt{2}}$, $\tan 45° = 1$.

6.3 Trigonometrical Relationships

We have considered the basic relationships, sine, cosine and tangent. The reciprocals of these are also important and are as follows:

the reciprocal of sin θ,
i.e. $1/\sin\theta$ is known as *cosecant* θ (cosec)

the reciprocal of cos θ,
i.e. $1/\cos\theta$ is known as *secant* θ (sec)

the reciprocal of tan θ,
i.e. $1/\tan\theta$ is known as *cotangent* θ (cot).

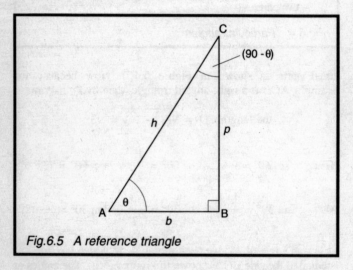

Fig.6.5 A reference triangle

Furthermore in any right-angled triangle such as is shown in Figure 6.5:

$$\sin\angle ACB = \sin(90-\theta)° = AB/AC$$

i.e. b/h which is equal to cos θ, so proving that

$$\cos\theta = \sin(90-\theta)°.$$

Similarly it can be shown that

$$\sin \theta = \cos (90 - \theta)° .$$

Also by Pythagoras' Theorem, from Figure 6.5:

$$p^2 + b^2 = h^2$$

Now because

$$\sin \theta = p/h, \text{ then } p = h \sin \theta \text{ so that } p^2 = h^2\sin^2 \theta,$$

also because

$$\cos \theta = b/h, \text{ then } b = h \cos \theta \text{ so that } b^2 = h^2\cos^2 \theta$$

so that

$$h^2\sin^2 \theta + h^2\cos^2 \theta = h^2$$

and on cancelling by h^2:

$$\sin^2 \theta + \cos^2 \theta = 1$$

a useful relationship which should be remembered especially because it leads to others as shown next.

Divide both sides by $\cos^2 \theta$:

$$\tan^2 \theta + 1 = 1/\cos^2 \theta = \sec^2 \theta$$

$$\therefore \qquad \sec^2 \theta - \tan^2 \theta = 1$$

Divide both sides by $\sin^2 \theta$:

$$1 + \frac{\cos^2 \theta}{\sin^2 \theta} = \frac{1}{\sin^2 \theta}$$

i.e.

$$1 + \cot^2 \theta = \operatorname{cosec}^2 \theta$$

$$\therefore \qquad \operatorname{cosec}^2 \theta - \cot^2 \theta = 1$$

6.3.1 Multiple Angle Formulae

We have now reached the stage where it can be appreciated that the normal rules used for reducing mathematical expressions or for solving equations cannot all be extended for use in trigonometry. A little thought shows that sin (A + B) cannot be expanded to sin A + sin B as might at first be expected. Again sin A . sin B is not equal to sin A . B so we must keep this in mind in what follows. (Note that here the full stop means 'multiplied by'.)

Consider the two angles A and B in the right-angled triangle OPQ as in Figure 6.6.

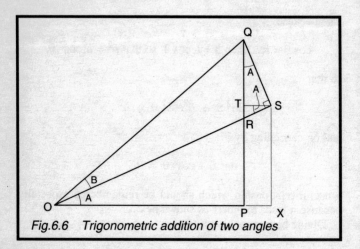

Fig.6.6   Trigonometric addition of two angles

sin POQ, i.e. sin (A + B) = PQ/OQ.

Let OR be extended to S and QS drawn so that ∠RSQ is a right-angle.

Draw a perpendicular ST from S onto PQ and also from SX onto OX.

Then ∠OSX = (90 – A)° and ∠RST = A (because TS and PX are parallel – Fig. 5.4).

Also ∠TSQ = (90 – A)°, hence ∠TQS = A. Then:

$$\sin (A + B) = \frac{PQ}{OQ} = \frac{PT + QT}{OQ} = \frac{PT}{OQ} + \frac{QT}{OQ}$$

also: $PT = SX = OS.\sin A$ and $QT = QS.\cos A$

hence:
$$\sin(A + B) = \frac{OS}{OQ} \sin A + \frac{QS}{OQ} \cos A$$

and since $\dfrac{OS}{OQ} = \cos B$ and $\dfrac{QS}{OQ} = \sin B$:

$$\sin (A + B) = \sin A.\cos.B + \cos A.\sin B. \qquad ....(i)$$

By using similar reasoning it can be shown that:

$$\sin (A - B) = \sin A.\cos B - \cos A.\sin B. \qquad ....(ii)$$

$$\cos (A+ B) = \cos A.\cos B - \sin A.\sin B. \qquad ....(iii)$$

$$\cos (A - B) = \cos A.\cos B + \sin A.\sin B. \qquad ....(iv)$$

Also $\tan (A + B) = \dfrac{\tan A + \tan B}{1 - \tan A \tan B}$ ....(v)

$$\tan (A - B) = \frac{\tan A - \tan B}{1 + \tan A \tan B} \qquad ....(vi)$$

We can use these relationships to develop others, e.g. by subtracting (iii) from (iv):

$$2 \sin A.\sin B = \cos (A - B) - \cos (A + B)$$

$$\therefore \sin A.\sin B = \frac{1}{2} \cos (A - B) - \frac{1}{2} \cos (A + B)$$

Similarly by adding equations (i) and (ii):

$$2 \sin A.\cos B = \sin (A + B) + \sin (A - B)$$

Also $2 \cos A \sin B = \sin (A + B) - \sin (A - B)$, and

$$2 \cos A \cos B = \cos (A + B) + \cos (A - B).$$

123

These equations are employed when we wish to express the product of two trigonometric ratios in the form of a sum.

Next by substituting $(C + D)/2$ for A and $(C - D)/2$ for B, then $A + B = C$ and $A - B = D$.

$$\therefore \quad \sin C + \sin D = 2 \sin \frac{C + D}{2} \cos \frac{C - D}{2}$$

$$\sin C - \sin D = 2 \cos \frac{C + D}{2} \sin \frac{C - D}{2}$$

$$\cos C + \cos D = 2 \cos \frac{C + D}{2} \cos \frac{C - D}{2}$$

$$\cos C - \cos D = 2 \sin \frac{C + D}{2} \sin \frac{D - C}{2}$$

(note the reversal in the last term).

Here the sum of two trigonometrical ratios is expressed in the form of a product.

Generally therefore by recalling equations (i) to (iv) in the following condensed form:

$$\sin (A \pm B) = \sin A.\cos B \pm \cos A.\sin B \qquad ....(vii)$$

$$\cos (A \pm B) = \cos A.\cos B -\!/\!+ \sin A.\sin B \qquad ....(viii)$$

we can then add or subtract pairs of these to obtain other relationships in which trigonometric forms of angles are either added or multiplied together.

By letting $A = B$ we can now develop the double angle formulae:

From (i) $\qquad \sin 2A = 2 \sin A.\cos A \qquad\qquad ....(ix)$

and similarly from (iii):

$$\cos 2A = \cos2 A - \sin2 A \qquad\qquad ....(x)$$

{don't forget that $\cos^2 A$ is shorthand for $(\cos A)^2$}

and from (v)
$$\tan 2A = \frac{2 \tan A}{1 - \tan^2 A}$$

Furthermore from $\cos 2A = \cos^2 A - \sin^2 A$

and $\sin^2 A + \cos^2 A = 1$ (Sect. 6.3),

$$\sin^2 A = \tfrac{1}{2}(1 - \cos 2A) \quad \cos^2 A = \tfrac{1}{2}(1 + \cos 2A) \quad ....(xi)$$

Here is a tricky one based on what we have done so far. It is to take the quantity cos 3A and express it in terms of cos A only. This is a useful exercise because it brings to light the many pit falls which may beset us.

$$\cos 3A = \cos (2A + A)$$

from (viii):

$$= \cos 2A \cos A - \sin 2A \sin A$$

and from (xi), since
$$2 \cos^2 A = 1 + \cos 2A$$

and also from (ix):

$$\cos 3A = (2\cos^2 A - 1) \cos A - (2 \sin A \cos A) \sin A.$$
$$= 2 \cos^3 A - \cos A - 2 \sin^2 A.\cos A$$
$$= 2 \cos^3 A - \cos A - 2(1 - \cos^2 A) \cos A$$

(from Sect. 6.3)

$$= 2 \cos^3 A - \cos A - 2 \cos A + 2 \cos^3 A$$
$$= 4 \cos^3 A - 3 \cos A$$

We seem to have plodded through a host of trigonometric relationships here but it is worth doing because they facilitate the solution of many electronics and telecommunications engineering problems. Here is just one example – it is concerned with the addition of two separate sine waves of the same amplitude (V) but at different frequencies, f_1 and f_2. The waves follow a sine rule (more of this in Sect. 6.5) and on addition the instantaneous voltage:

125

$$v = V (\sin 2\pi f_1 t + \sin 2\pi f_2 t)$$

where f_1 and f_2 represent the frequencies and t, a time elapsed. Note here that these are two separate frequencies linked by a plus sign.

To see what happens when the two combine we use the formula quoted above for sin C + sin D where C = $2\pi f_1 t$ and D = $2\pi f_2 t$. Hence:

$$v = V \left\{ 2 \sin \frac{2\pi f_1 t + 2\pi f_2 t}{2} \cdot \cos \frac{2\pi f_1 t - 2\pi f_2 t}{2} \right\}$$

$$\therefore \quad v = 2V \left\{ \sin 2\pi \frac{(f_1 + f_2)t}{2} \cdot \cos 2\pi \frac{(f_1 - f_2)t}{2} \right\}$$

the formula therefore indicates that the combined wave consists of a frequency determined by the sum of the two frequencies involved, modulated by a frequency equal to the difference between them. The original sign of addition between the two waves has now become one of multiplication and a new frequency (the *beat* frequency) is generated.

6.3.2 Some Formulae for any Triangle

So far we have been limited to discussion of right-angled triangles only. In this Section trigonometric rules are considered for triangles of any dimension and shape. Figure 6.7 shows such a triangle in which there is no right angle. Its angles are labelled A, B and C and the sides opposite these angles are a, b and c as shown.

The *sine rule* is easily remembered. It states that in any triangle, the ratios of the sines of the angles to the length of the opposite sides are identical, i.e.

$$\frac{a}{\sin A} = \frac{b}{\sin B} = \frac{c}{\sin C}$$

The *cosine rule* may be a little more difficult to remember but nevertheless it is of equal importance. There is a different equation for each angle:

126

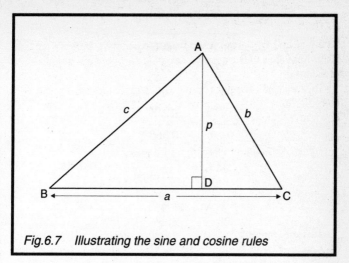

Fig.6.7   Illustrating the sine and cosine rules

$$a^2 = b^2 + c^2 - 2bc \cos A$$

$$b^2 = a^2 + c^2 - 2ac \cos B$$

$$c^2 = a^2 + b^2 - 2ab \cos C$$

These two sets of rules are sufficient for the solution of many problems, there are also several other formulae which have been developed, these are not quoted here otherwise we will hardly be able to see the wood for the trees.

In the triangle of Figure 6.7 let $a = 22$, $b = 12$ and the angle $C = 60°$. We determine the values of angles A and B and also the side c.

Using the cosine rule:

$$c^2 = 22^2 + 12^2 - 2 \times 22 \times 12 . \cos C =$$

$$= 628 - (528 \times 0.5) = 628 - 264$$

$$\therefore \quad c^2 = 364 \quad \text{and} \quad c = 19.079 .$$

We now know the lengths of all the sides and the value of one angle, the sine rule is now appropriate:

$$\frac{a}{\sin A} = \frac{c}{\sin C}$$

$$\therefore \quad \frac{22}{\sin A} = \frac{19.08}{\sin 60°}$$

$$\therefore \quad \frac{22}{\sin A} = \frac{19.08}{0.866}$$

$$\therefore \quad \sin A = \frac{22 \times 0.866}{19.08} = 0.9985$$

$$\therefore \quad A = 86.9°$$

Also
$$\frac{b}{\sin B} = \frac{c}{\sin C}$$

$$\therefore \quad \frac{12}{\sin B} = \frac{19.08}{0.866}$$

$$\therefore \quad \sin B = \frac{12 \times 0.866}{19.08} = 0.5447$$

$$\therefore \quad B = 33.0°$$

Adding the three angles together gives 179.9°, a clear enough indication that our calculations are correct.

Area of a Triangle – referring to Figure 6.7, if the perpendicular AD is known, then the area of the triangle is simply $(a \times p)/2$. Also $p = c \sin B$, hence:

$$\text{area of triangle} = \tfrac{1}{2} ac \sin B ,$$

i.e. one half of the product of two of the sides and the sine of the included angle.

6.4 Vectors

It is here that we ought to pause in order to appreciate the use of *vectors* which are important in mathematics and essential in electronics. A vector is a quantity which possesses both *magnitude* and *direction*. In electronics the magnitude and direction may be represented by a line of known length and which is at an angle with some *reference axis*. On the other hand a *scalar* quantity is one which possesses magnitude alone and so, in not representing direction, a reference axis is not required.

As an example, the statement that an aircraft is flying at 500 km/h gives information on its speed only, we do not know in which direction it is flying. The speed of 500 km/h, like those representing time, length, weight, area, temperature, etc., is clearly a scalar quantity for it is fully expressed by a single number. If directional information is added, say that the aircraft is flying due South, then a vector quantity has been created which now involves both magnitude and direction. As mentioned above, a reference must be involved, for an aircraft the reference is known world-wide as North which is labelled 0° thus the direction South is completely specified by the figure 180°. Diagrammatically a vector quantity is illustrated by a line of definite length representing the magnitude and drawn at the appropriate angle relative to the reference with an arrow added to show the direction. Thus our aircraft vector would be as in Figure 6.8(i), a line of length , say 5 cm pointing downwards.

6.4.1 Addition of Vectors

For navigation this single vector does not tell the whole story because aircraft must take into account the effects of air currents. Vectors can be added geometrically so the net effect of all forces acting on the aircraft can be determined to establish the true direction. Consider a West to East wind with a speed of say, 100 km/h through which the aircraft is flying. The vector of the wind is as shown in (ii) indicating how the air surrounding the aircraft is moving, in this case causing it to have a velocity sideways from its intended track. To find the actual path taken by the aircraft, the two vectors must be added. This is by completion of the parallelogram as shown in (iii). In this particular case and also in many we meet in electronics, the two vectors are at 90° to each other and the parallelogram therefore becomes a rectangle. Furthermore we will see later that frequently a triangle is sufficient.

In (iii) let the aircraft be at point O. It has two velocities, OA, its own and OW, that of the air. The rectangle OAPW is completed and the diagonal drawn. The diagonal is then the vector representing the resultant of the other two, i.e. it shows the actual velocity (both speed and direction) of the aircraft (note that velocity includes direction whereas speed does not). OP and θ can be measured or calculated:

OAP is a right angle therefore:

$$OP^2 = OA^2 + AP^2$$

but $$AP = OW$$

$\therefore$ $$OP^2 = 500^2 + 100^2$$

from which $$OP = 509.9 \text{ km/h}$$

and $$\tan \theta = \frac{100}{500} = 0.2$$

$\therefore$ $$\theta \approx 11.31° \text{ or equally } 11° \, 18.6'$$

Relative to North the aircraft flight track is therefore $180° - 11.3° = 168.7°$.

This is a simple example of the use of vectors and is useful as an introduction to the subject.

It is clear that when two vectors are added, their sum is the displacement which is equivalent to the combined effect of the two individual displacements. In Figure 6.8 the two vectors which are added are at 90°, the vector diagram therefore being a rectangle as shown. Generally however vectors are added by completion of a parallelogram (a rectangle is in fact one form of parallelogram) as shown in Figure 6.9. Here OA and OB are the two vectors to be added, the parallelogram OACB is completed and the diagonal OC drawn. This diagonal through O is the resultant of the two vectors OA and OB. Pythagoras is of no help here because the parallelogram contains no right angles as

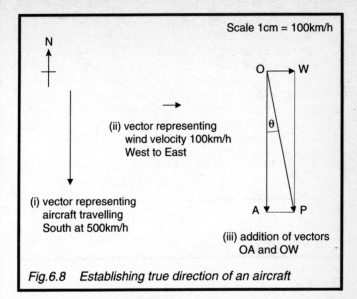

Scale 1cm = 100km/h

N

O → W

θ

(ii) vector representing
wind velocity 100km/h
West to East

(i) vector representing
aircraft travelling
South at 500km/h

A ↓ → P

(iii) addition of vectors
OA and OW

Fig.6.8   Establishing true direction of an aircraft

in the example above, therefore extend OB and drop a perpendicular CD on it, see Figure 6.9. Now we need the cosine rule
(Sect. 6.3.2) firstly with regard to the triangle OBC:

$$OC^2 = BC^2 + OB^2 - 2BC.OB \cos \angle OBC$$

and therefore

$$OC^2 = OA^2 + OB^2 + 2OA.OB \cos \phi \quad (\cos 180 - \phi = -\cos \phi)$$

$$OC = \sqrt{(OA^2 + OB^2 + 2OA.OB \cos \phi)}$$

We find the two angles θ_1 and θ_2 separately:

$$\tan \theta_1 = \frac{CD}{OD} = \frac{BC \sin \phi}{OB + BD} = \frac{OA \sin \phi}{OB + BC \cos \phi}$$

$$= \frac{OA \sin \phi}{OB + OA \cos \phi}$$

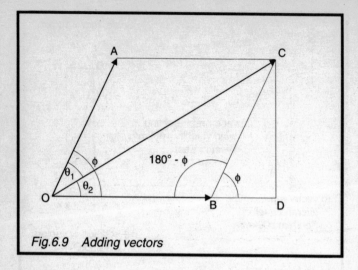

Fig.6.9   Adding vectors

Similarly:

$$\tan \theta_2 = \frac{OB \sin \phi}{OA + OB \cos \phi}$$

6.4.2   Subtraction of Vectors

There is little difficulty here for a vector to be subtracted is simply drawn at 180° from what it would have been if it were to be added, in other words adding a minus sign to a vector is equivalent to rotating it through 180°.

6.4.3   Resolution of Vectors

Just as two vectors can be combined to find their resultant (Fig. 6.9) so equally a vector can be resolved into two components, usually and especially in the case of electronics, at right-angles to each other. Accordingly in Figure 6.10 the vector OP is resolved into two components mutually at right-angles, OA and OB which, acting together, could replace it. Then:

$$OA = OP \cos \theta \qquad \qquad ....(i)$$

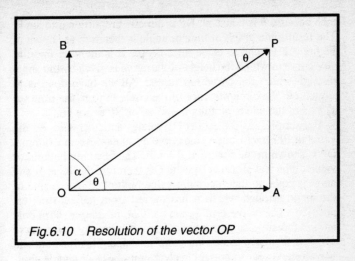

Fig.6.10   Resolution of the vector OP

$$OB = OP \sin \theta$$

Also since $\angle BOP = (90 - \theta)^\circ = \alpha^\circ$

then $$OB = OP \cos (90 - \theta)^\circ = OP \cos \alpha^\circ \quad ....(ii).$$

From (i) and (ii) it is evident that in cases such as that above, the resolved part of a vector in any given direction is equal to the magnitude of the vector multiplied by the cosine of the angle it makes with that direction.

The manipulation of vectors, especially for the solution of electronics problems, is considered in greater detail in Chapter 8.

6.5 Sine and Cosine Curves

If a graph of the values of the sine function is plotted from 0 – 360°, also allowing for changes between positive and negative, the result is the *sine curve*, or in electronics the *sine wave*, repeating every 360°.

Let us go back to Figure 6.1 and consider the length of NP as OP rotates through the four quadrants, also recalling that NP is related to the angle θ by the sine function, i.e. NP = $h \sin \theta$, then because *h* is constant, NP is directly proportional to sin θ. The result on a graph of time or angle is therefore as shown in Figure 6.11(i) and to electronics people it is the very familiar sine curve in which the height of the curve is given by the angle through which the curve has turned. All we have done is to stretch out the circumference of the circle to form the time (or *x*) axis of the wave, plotting the value of NP as we go.

Put simply, as the radius OP rotates anticlockwise, so the value of PN traces out a sine curve as shown. As an example, OP is shown in the Figure at θ = 60°. The maximum height or value of the waveform is equal to OP, therefore the value at any point is equal to the maximum value multiplied by the sine of the angle through which it has moved from the zero or rest position. The waveform graph is that of *simple harmonic motion* (s.h.m. – as with a pendulum), it is simply a sine curve and it is then said to be *sinusoidal* in shape. This fundamental waveform is very important in electronics because simple alternating currents and voltages are of this form. A good example is that of the electricity supply mains which we describe next because the method of generation follows s.h.m. so closely.

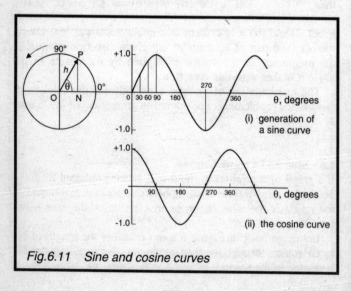

Fig.6.11   Sine and cosine curves

The simplest mechanical alternating voltage generator consists of a single loop of wire which is rotated within a magnetic field as shown in the sketch of Figure 6.12. The *armature* which holds the wires and rotates them is not shown but the elementary current-collecting device is, that is, the two *slip rings*, S_1 and S_2 on which rub two fixed *carbon brushes*. The slip rings are insulated from each other and each is connected to one side of the loop. The brushes maintain electrical contact with the rotating slip rings and themselves are connected to the external circuit. The direction of current flow shown by the arrows is that of electron flow, the sides of the loop ab and cd cutting the flux and producing induced voltages which are in series and therefore adding. Larger voltages are generated by increasing the number of turns on the coil.

Clearly when the loop is in the position shown, the *rate* of cutting flux and the induced electromotive force are greatest. When it has turned through 90°, the wires ab and cd are running parallel with the flux, cutting none and therefore the voltage induced is zero.

It may be instructive however, rather than to assume that a sine wave is generated, to prove it instead. This can be done

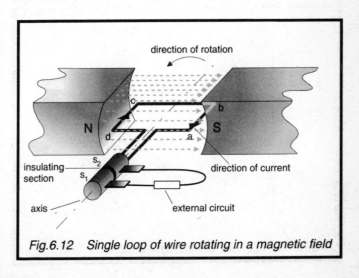

Fig.6.12   *Single loop of wire rotating in a magnetic field*

by considering the component of motion of a wire which is at right angles to the flux lines because it is this component which generates the e.m.f. Consider Figure 6.13 which shows a wire W travelling in a circle of centre O in a magnetic field. Its velocity at any instant can be illustrated by the vector (Sect. 6.4) WX. This is resolved into the two vectors WE and WI as shown. Now WI is parallel to the lines of magnetic flux therefore is ineffective, on the other hand WE crosses the flux at right-angles and is therefore fully effective in producing an e.m.f.

It is evident that if the angle between OW and Oy' be designated θ, then $\angle OWE$ is also θ, $\angle EWX = (90 - \theta)°$ and $\angle EXW = \theta$. Now in the triangle EWX:

$$\frac{EW}{WX} = \sin \theta \qquad \therefore EW = WX \sin \theta$$

and if we call EW, v_e

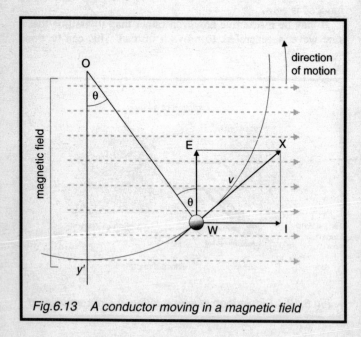

Fig.6.13   *A conductor moving in a magnetic field*

then $v_e = v \sin \theta$ proving that as the wire rotates through the magnetic flux , the effective velocity which produces the e.m.f. is equal to the actual conductor velocity multiplied by the sine of the angle through which its radius has turned, proving that a sine wave is generated.

We will also find that electronic oscillators, unless used as generators of square, pulse, saw-toothed waves, etc., automatically produce sine waves.

A glance at the sine and cosine trigonometric tables shows that in the first quadrant $(0 - 90°)$ the value of sine θ runs from 0 to 1 whereas that of cosine θ is from 1 down to 0. A cosine curve is shown at (ii) in Figure 6.11, this is generated by the projection of ON instead of that of PN as for the sine wave.

The cosine curve is identical in shape to that of the sine wave and generally in everyday life, the fact that we show it as being 90° out of phase with a sine wave from the same generator is of little consequence, for example although we generally consider that the electric mains is a sine wave, it is in fact equally a cosine wave. In more advanced mathematics however the difference between sine and cosine waves may be more important.

We will not study tan θ here except to note that because

$$\tan \theta = \frac{\sin \theta}{\cos \theta} \, ,$$

it is clear that at $\theta = 0°$, tan $\theta = 0$ (because $\sin \theta = 0$), however at $\theta = 90°$, tan θ becomes infinitely large (because now $\cos \theta = 0$).

Chapter 7

SERIES

A *series* is a sequence of numbers in which each number is related to the previous one by some known rule. The series 1, 2, 3... is the simplest, the rule of course being to add 1 to any number to obtain the next. A series like this in which a constant quantity is added to each term to produce the next is known as an *arithmetical progression*. On the other hand, a series in which each term is calculated by multiplying the previous term by the same amount is known as a *geometrical progression*. Here a simple example is given by 1, 5, 25, 125... in which each successive term is multiplied by 5 to produce the next term. We look at these two types of series first, following which we grapple with the Binomial Theorem, one of the most useful in mathematics.

Generally in any series only a few of the early terms need to be given for these are usually sufficient to indicate the underlying law.

7.1 Arithmetical Progression

As indicated above, we might define an arithmetical progression as a series in which any term is formed by adding the same quantity (d – which may be positive or negative) to the preceding term. Thus 8, 16, 24, 32... are in arithmetical progression and so are 32, 24, 16, 8..., the same quantity, +8 or –8 being involved at each move. Here $d = 8$ and we can see that the general form of an arithmetical progression is a, $(a + d)$, $(a + 2d)$... where a is the first term.

The rth term is given by $a + (r - 1)d$ for as is seen above where $d = +8$, the 4th term is $8 + (4 - 1)8 = 32$ or when $d = -8$, the 4th term is now 8.

Let n be the total number of terms and l the last term:

Then $$l = a + (n - 1)d \qquad \text{....(i)}$$

Now let S denote the sum of n terms, then:

$$S = a + (a + d) + (a + 2d) + \ldots + (l - 2d) + (l - d) + l$$

next add the series in the reverse order:

$$S = l + (l - d) + (l - 2d) + \ldots + (a + 2d) + (a + d) + a$$

to give:

$$2S = (a + l) + (a + l) + \ldots \text{to } n \text{ terms} = n(a + l)$$

hence

$$S = \frac{n}{2}(a + l)$$

i.e. when the first and last terms are known, the sum of n terms is given (which can be checked with our series above).

Next, substituting the value of l from (i):

$$S = \frac{n}{2}\left\{ 2a + (n - 1)d \right\}$$

again giving the sum of n terms but now when the first term and the common difference are known.

As an example, suppose we wish to find the sum of the first n natural numbers. For this $a = 1$ and $d = 1$, then:

$$\text{sum} = \frac{n}{2}\left\{ 2a + (n - 1)d \right\} = n\frac{(n + 1)}{2}$$

e.g. when $n = 15$, $\quad \text{sum} = \dfrac{15(16)}{2} = 120$.

Again, to find the 15th term of the progression $1, 4, 7, 10, \ldots$

Here $a = 1$, $d = 3$, then:

$$l = a + (n - 1)d$$

in this case $\quad l = 1 + (14 \times 3) = 43$

140

Next to find the number of odd numbers there are from 1 to 99. We might guess this one but:

$$99 = 1 + (n-1)\,2 \quad \therefore \quad \frac{98}{2} = n-1 \quad \therefore \quad n = 50.$$

To find their sum:

$$s = \frac{n}{2}\left\{2a + (n-1)d\right\} = 25\left\{2 + (49 \times 2)\right\}$$

$$= 25 \times 100 = 2500.$$

7.2 Geometrical Progression

With a geometrical progression every term bears the same ratio (the *common ratio*) to the one before it. Hence if a is the first term and r is the common ratio, the second term is ar, the third is ar^2, the fourth ar^3, etc. Note that the index of r is one less than the number of the term, hence the nth term is ar^{n-1}.

To find the sum, S of n terms therefore:

$$S = a + ar + ar^2 + \ldots\ldots + ar^{n-2} + ar^{n-1}. \quad \ldots\text{(i)}$$

Now multiply each term by r to give:

$$Sr = ar + ar^2 + ar^3 + \ldots\ldots + ar^{n-1} + ar^n \quad \ldots\text{(ii)}$$

and on subtracting (i) from (ii):

$$Sr - S = ar^n - a \quad \therefore \quad S(r-1) = a(r^n - 1)$$

$$\therefore \qquad\qquad S = \frac{a(r^n - 1)}{r - 1} \qquad\qquad \ldots\text{(iii)}$$

which can also be stated as

$$S = \frac{a(1 - r^n)}{1 - r} \qquad\qquad \ldots\text{(iv)}$$

7.2.1 Sum to Infinity

From (iv), provided that the value of r lies *between* -1 and $+1$, then r^n decreases as n increases, hence in the limit when n approaches infinity, r^n tends to zero. The sum of a series to infinity is therefore:

$$S_\infty = \frac{a}{1-r}$$

As an example, we calculate the sum of the series $\frac{1}{2} + \frac{1}{4} + \frac{1}{8} + \frac{1}{16} \ldots\ldots$ to ∞.

Here $\quad a = 1/2, \quad r = 1/2,$ hence $S_\infty = \dfrac{1/2}{1 - 1/2} = 1.$

A geometrical progression may also be used to find the actual value of a recurring decimal. The sum to infinity as developed above is used, e.g. to find the value of $0.\dot{3}$ (the dot indicates a recurring figure):

$$0.\dot{3} = 0.3333 \ldots = 0 + 3/10 + 3/10^2 + 3/10^3 + \ldots$$

let this be equal to $0 + S$

Here $\qquad\qquad r = 0.1, \quad a = 0.3$

Then $\qquad S = \dfrac{0.3}{1 - 0.1} = \dfrac{0.3}{0.9} = \dfrac{1}{3}$

which we know to be correct because on changing $1/3$ into a decimal, the result is $0.\dot{3}$.

7.3 Binomial Theorem

This is a formula by which any power of a binomial (two names – i.e. two terms) can be determined without multiplying fully. We do not prove the theorem here as it is rather time-consuming but state it as the expansion of $(a + b)^n$.

$$(a + b)^n = a^n + na^{n-1}b + \frac{n(n-1)}{1 \times 2} \cdot a^{n-2}b^2 +$$

$$+ \frac{n(n-1)(n-2)}{1 \times 2 \times 3} \cdot a^{n-3}b^3 + \ldots + b^n$$

— a rather frightening expression, but manageable. (Note here that the denominator of the 4th term in the expression (2×3) would normally be written as $3!$ or $\lfloor 3$, meaning $1 \times 2 \times 3$. This is known as *factorial notation*. Hence $5!$ (or $\lfloor 5$) signifies $1 \times 2 \times 3 \times 4 \times 5$ $(= 120)$ and $r!$ would be $1 \times 2 \times 3 \ldots \times r$.)

The series on the right of the equals sign can terminate only when n is a positive whole number. When $n = 2$ therefore:

$$(a + b)^2 = a^2 + 2ab + \frac{2 \times 1b^2}{2} = a^2 + 2ab + b^2$$

and similarly when $n = 3$:

$$(a + b)^3 = a^3 + 3a^2b + 3ab^2 + b^3$$

Expansions for higher values of n are obtained similarly. Note from the above that:

(1) the highest index used is n, e.g. for $(a + b)^3$ it is 3, also the coefficient is 1;

(2) the indices of a decrease by 1 in each successive term;

(3) the indices of b increase by 1 in each successive term;

(4) the number of terms is 1 greater than the index.

From this it is possible to determine any term in a binomial expansion, e.g. the $(r + 1)^{th}$ term is given by:

$$\frac{n(n-1)(n-2)\ldots\ldots(n-r+1)}{r!} \cdot a^{n-r}b^r$$

so for example to find the 8th term of $(a + b)^{12}$:

$$r + 1 = 8 \quad \therefore \quad r = 7 \quad n = 12 \quad (n - r) = 5$$

the 8th term is therefore:

$$\frac{12.11.10......(12 - 7 + 1)}{7!} \; a^5 . b^7$$

$$= \; \frac{12.11.10.9.8.7.6}{2.3.4.5.6.7} \; a^5 . b^7 = 792 \; a^5 . b^7$$

7.3.1 Approximations

Using the binomial theorem we can expand $(1 + a)^n$ as follows:

$$(1 + a)^n = 1 + na + \frac{n(n - 1)}{2} \; a^2 + \; .....$$

however if a is small compared with 1, then a^2 will be very small, accordingly the first two terms of the expansion are often sufficiently accurate for many practical purposes. Hence

$$(1 + a)^n \approx 1 + na$$

as an example, to find the value of 1.06^3:

$$1.06^3 = (1 + 0.06)^3 = 1 + (3 \times 0.06) = 1.18$$

The correct answer is 1.191 so the approximate answer is frequently sufficient for many practical purposes. Let us try again to find the cube root of 1.05:

$$\sqrt[3]{1.05} = 1 + \frac{0.05}{3} = 1 + 0.0167 = 1.0167,$$

the more accurate answer being 1.0164.

7.4 Epsilon

We first met epsilon (e – but actually in Greek, ε) when considering it as the basis of Napieran logarithms, then again in graphical form in Section 4.2.6 and Figure 4.11(ii). There is little doubt that epsilon is a remarkable mathematical constant and that it is all around us in everyday life. In fact the ubiquitous e is found in a spider's web and in the shells of certain snails and other molluscs. These little creatures have practised advanced geometry without even knowing it!

Here we find out how the peculiar figure of 2.71828 for e arises. Let us consider an expression as derived from the Binomial Theorem, i.e.:

$$\left(1+\frac{1}{n}\right)^n = 1 + n \cdot 1^{n-1} \cdot \frac{1}{n} + \frac{n(n-1)}{1 \times 2} \cdot 1^{n-2} \cdot \frac{1}{n^2} +$$

$$+ \frac{n(n-1)(n-2)}{1 \times 2 \times 3} \cdot 1^{n-3} \cdot \frac{1}{n^3} + \ldots$$

we can immediately remove all terms such as 1^{n-1}, 1^{n-2}, etc., to leave:

$$\left(1+\frac{1}{n}\right)^n = 1 + 1 + \frac{1}{2}\left(1-\frac{1}{n}\right) +$$

$$+ \frac{1}{2 \times 3}\left(1-\frac{1}{n}\right)\left(1-\frac{2}{n}\right) \ldots +$$

and clearly the number of terms increases with the value of n, hence $\{1 + (1/n)^n\}$ must increase as n increases. However if n is less than infinite, then $\{1 + (1/n)^n\}$ must itself be less than the total of the expression to infinity. In fact from the above expression it is clearly less than 3 and so as n tends towards infinity, $\{1 + (1/n)^n\}$ tends towards a finite limit which we denote by epsilon (e or ε). Hence:

$$e = 1 + 1 + \frac{1}{2!} + \frac{1}{3!} \ldots + \frac{1}{r!} + \ldots \text{ to } \infty$$

and we can use this series to calculate the value of e to any

145

degree of accuracy required. Computers of course do this with ease. For our part let us calculate the value of e to 4 decimal places:

$1 + 1 + 1/2 = 2.5000$ $1/3! = 1/6 = 0.1667$
$1/4! = 1/24 = 0.0417$ $1/5! = 1/120 = 0.0083$
$1/6! = 1/720 = 0.0014$ $1/7! = 1/5040 = 0.0002$

Adding we get 2.7183 which is a sufficiently good answer, knowing that e is generally quoted as 2.718 28 .... Had we worked to 6 decimal places, this is the result we would have obtained.

From this it can be shown that:

$$e^x = 1 + x + \frac{x^2}{2!} + \frac{x^3}{3!} + ... \frac{x^r}{r!} + ...$$

and therefore

$$e^{ax} = 1 + ax + \frac{a^2x^2}{2!} + \frac{a^3x^3}{3!} + ... \frac{a^rx^r}{r!} + ...$$

and by letting a $= -1$

$$e^{-x} = 1 - x + \frac{x^2}{2!} - \frac{x^3}{3!} + ... (-1)^r . \frac{x^r}{r!} + ...$$

As an example, let us calculate the value of e^x to three decimal places when $x = 1.5$.

$(1 + x) = 2.5$ $x^2/2 = 1.125$

$x^3/3! = 0.5625$ $x^4/4! = 0.2109$

$x^5/5! = 0.0633$ $x^6/6! = 0.0158$

$x^7/7! = 0.0034$

Adding and correcting to 3 decimal places we get 4.481 (by calculator, 4.4817).

Binomial distributions are especially useful in statistical work, e.g. in the study of *probability* (the extent to which an event is likely to occur) – see Section 9.3.

7.5 Fourier Series

Jean-Baptiste Joseph Fourier was a French mathematician and physicist who produced his most famous work around the move into the 19th century. His theorem which concerns us here is with regard to *continuous periodic functions*, meaning continuous waves with all cycles the same. This particular work was published in 1807. Being periodic means that the cycles recur regularly, they therefore have a *fundamental* frequency. Fourier considered that any complex wave consists of a fundamental frequency together with a set of harmonics at frequencies which are whole number multiples of it. This theorem applies to all kinds of electrical waves and even sound waves. The process of determining the amplitude of the harmonics is known as *Fourier analysis*. Of interest is the fact that within our ears, the *cochlea* is lined with a membrane containing feathery hair cells which resonate to the various harmonics present and essentially they carry out a Fourier analysis of the incoming sound to present to the brain. There is a multiplicity of waves which can be so analysed but by considering only a few of the regular and well-known ones it is possible for us to appreciate the basic idea of waveform analysis. Remember that Fourier analysis considers continuous functions hence it is not possible to analyse a wave which varies in shape from cycle to cycle.

Here we consider the general statement of the theorem that certain waveforms can be expressed as the sum of a number of sine (and cosine) waves, each of different amplitude and frequency. It is perhaps not easy to appreciate that the square wave which is so angular consists of nothing more than smooth sine waves but this is easily proved both mathematically and graphically. Fourier of course used more advanced mathematics than we have at our disposal, hence this excursion into his techniques must be limited mainly to stating the results rather than deriving them.

In general mathematical terms therefore Fourier's theorem states that any periodic function $f(x)$ may be represented by the sum of a single constant term (a_0) together with a series of sines and cosines of its multiples, e.g.:

$$f(x) = a_0 + a_1 \cos x + a_2 \cos 2x + a_3 \cos 3x + ...$$
$$+ b_1 \sin x + b_2 \sin 2x + b_3 \sin 3x + ...$$

We can restate this in an electrical form where e is the net voltage:

$$e = c + a_1 \sin \omega t + a_2 \sin 2\omega t + a_3 \sin 3\omega t + ...$$
$$+ b_1 \cos \omega t + b_2 \cos 2\omega t + b_3 \cos 3\omega t + ... \quad \text{(i)}$$

where c is a constant which can be shown to be the mean value of the wave over one cycle. ω is equal to 2π times the wave frequency and t is the time elapsed from commencement of the wave.

Next it is important to understand the meaning of *phase*. This is perhaps best appreciated from an example. If two waves of the same wavelength start from the same point together they will always be in step and they are then said to be *in phase*. However if starting at different times, they would always be out of step and the crests or troughs of one wave would not coincide with those of the other. The two waves are then said to be *out of phase*. To quote phase as a measurement there must therefore be some fixed datum point. However this may be unnecessary when considering phase differences between two waves e.g. if the phase difference is 90° then one wave is at its peak when the other is at zero and clearly if the phase difference is 180°, the two waves are in opposition.

Now from equation (vii) of Section 6.3.1:

$$A \sin (\omega t + \phi) = A \sin \omega t \cos \phi + A \cos \omega t \sin \phi,$$

which can be expressed as $a \sin \omega t + b \cos \omega t$ where $a = A \cos \phi$ and $b = A \sin \phi$, hence $a_1 \sin \omega t + b_1 \cos \omega t$ can be expressed as $A_1 \sin (\omega t + \phi_1)$ and similarly with the other pairs of components. Hence:

$$e = c + E_1 \sin (\omega t + \phi_1) + E_2 \sin (2\omega t + \phi_2) +$$
$$+ E_3 \sin (3\omega t + \phi_3) + ...$$

148

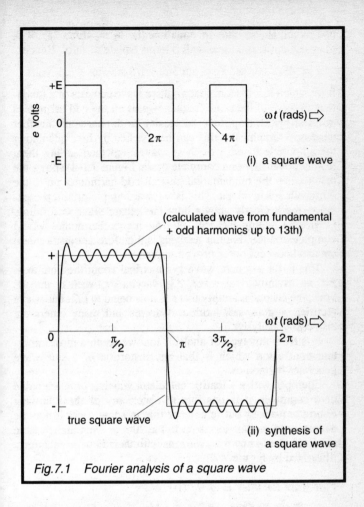

+E

e volts

0

2π 4π ωt (rads) ⇨

-E

(i) a square wave

(calculated wave from fundamental
+ odd harmonics up to 13th)

+

0        $\pi/2$ π $3\pi/2$ 2π ωt (rads) ⇨

-

true square wave

(ii) synthesis of
a square wave

Fig.7.1   Fourier analysis of a square wave

where E_1 and E_2 are the maximum values of the various components and ϕ_1, ϕ_2 .... the phase angles. This expression forms the basis of many analyses of electronic systems.

The use of these formulae can be illustrated by considering the extremely angular square wave. Such a wave varying between +E and –E is shown in Figure 7.1(i). The mean value over one cycle is zero, hence $c = 0$. Further mathematical endeavour shows that in equation (i), $a_1 = 4E/\pi$, $a_2 = 0$, $a_3 = 4E/3\pi$, $a_4 = 0$ .... and all b terms equate to zero. Hence:

$$e = 4E/\pi \, (\sin \omega t + 1/3 \sin 3\omega t + 1/5 \sin 5\omega t + ...) \text{ volts}$$

from which it is evident that a square wave consists of a fundamental wave of the same frequency plus all the odd harmonics to infinity with amplitude decreasing as the harmonic number increases. Graphically this can be checked by first calculating the amplitude of each of these waves and then adding them together over half or a complete cycle. Figure 7.1(ii) shows the result when the fundamental plus all odd harmonics up to the thirteenth are involved. This is a rewarding pictorial representation for it clearly shows how the square wave is forming. Obviously adding the 15th and all higher harmonics would complete the job. Fourier analysis is therefore not just a mathematical concept but is proved in practice.

This is for a square wave symmetrical about the time axis. For an asymmetrical wave, e.g. varying between 0 and +E volts, the change is simply that c is now equal to E/2. Full-wave rectifier outputs, saw-tooth waveforms and many others are also easily analysed.

It is from this type of analysis that we reach a most important conclusion which is that any distortion of a sine wave generates harmonics.

Equipped with a scientific calculator which is programmable or a computer, it is possible to check any of the following Fourier equations but remember that in some cases it may be necessary to include terms up to the 20th or even higher. Here are a few well-known waveforms with their Fourier equations, illustrated by Figure 7.2.:

Full-Wave Rectifier {Fig. 7.2(i)}

$$e = \frac{2E}{\pi} - \frac{4E}{\pi} \left(\frac{\cos 2\omega t}{3} + \frac{\cos 4\omega t}{15} + \frac{\cos 6\omega t}{35} + ... \right) \text{volts}$$

where in each fraction within the brackets $\cos n\omega t$ is divided by $(n + 1)(n - 1)$. Here there is a constant c, this is what a full-wave rectifier is designed for, i.e. $c = 2E/\pi$. Only even harmonics are generated.

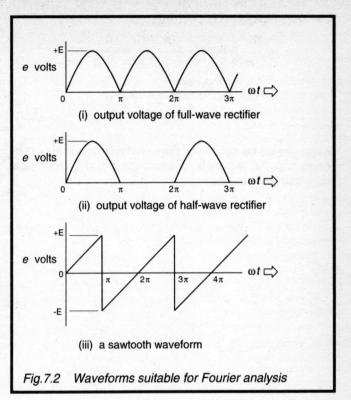

(i) output voltage of full-wave rectifier

(ii) output voltage of half-wave rectifier

(iii) a sawtooth waveform

Fig.7.2   Waveforms suitable for Fourier analysis

Half-Wave Rectifier {Fig. 7.2(ii)}
As in the full wave case the constant c has a value but now it is reduced to half, i.e. c = E/π.

$$e = \frac{E}{\pi} + E\left(\frac{\sin \omega t}{2} - \frac{2 \cos 2\omega t}{3\pi} - \right.$$

$$\left. - \frac{2 \cos 4\omega t}{15\pi} - \frac{2 \cos 6\omega t}{35\pi} - ....\right) \text{ volts}$$

there are even harmonics only.

151

Saw Tooth Waveform {Fig. 7.2(iii)}

$$e = \frac{2E}{\pi} \left(\sin \omega t - \frac{\sin 2\omega t}{2} + \frac{\sin 3\omega t}{3} - \right.$$

$$\left. - \frac{\sin 4\omega t}{4} + ... \right) \text{ volts}$$

Fourier equations for many other waveforms are also published, e.g. for the unidirectional square wave, rectangular wave, triangular wave.

Chapter 8

COMPLEX ALGEBRA

When we studied vectors in Section 6.4 we were concerned with the magnitude of a quantity and its direction only. These could be represented by a line of known length and with the angle made with a reference axis. Now a further complication arises which is that of *time,* i.e. we must consider mathematically conditions which are not happening simultaneously. Therefore although still mainly on the subject of vectors, the techniques we have to use in *complex algebra* warrant a chapter on their own.

Phase is a term which we may not have met before, it is one used with regard to electrical waveforms and it is defined as a point within the cycle relative to a fixed datum point. It is measured in degrees or radians. When a line is used in electronics to indicate magnitude and relative phase of for example, a current, voltage or impedance, it is then known as a *phasor*. The difficulty is therefore, how can we use phasors when things in a circuit are not happening at the same time.

Here we meet again the mysterious *imaginary* quantity first mentioned in Section 3.2.3 and in this Chapter we will understand more clearly what its functions are. Because the square of both positive and negative numbers is positive, then there can be no real root of a negative number, for example $x^2 = -1$ has no normal solution. This is highlighted by the formula for solving a quadratic equation, an example being $x^2 - 4x + 13$ which when solved gives $x = 2 +/- \sqrt{-9}$. Accordingly an *operator* was invented which when squared was equal to -1 and in electronics this is labelled "j" (in non-electrical work "i" is used), j is therefore equal to the square root of -1, i.e. $j = \sqrt{-1}$ and $j^2 = -1$. Using the same example, $j3 \times j3 = j^2 \times 9 = -9$, i.e. $\sqrt{-9} = j3$.

When first considered there was much confusion over the apparent breakdown of reality so these numbers were called "imaginary" but it is important to realize that it is not a question of being only in the imagination but more as an image or reflection. In electronics capacitance and inductance give rise

153

to such numbers and there is nothing imaginary about them, they are every bit as effective as so-called real numbers. Quantities with both real and imaginary parts are said to be "complex" hence the system is generally known as Complex Algebra, Complex Notation or simply Complex Numbers. In electronics the technique, although seemingly complicated at first sight, simply operates on the rectangular coordinates of phasors and in so doing enables us to build up equations in which the two coordinates are kept apart, this is the main use of the operator j. Let us first appreciate how this operator functions.

8.1   j in the Four Quadrants

The four quadrants are illustrated in Figure 8.1(i). The 3 o'clock axis is taken as the reference and rotation is anti-clockwise. This is the *real* axis. At 90° is the *imaginary* axis labelled j so we can perhaps define j as an operator which rotates an axis by 90° anti-clockwise. Accordingly a further multiplication by j reaches the real axis again but now in a negative direction, resulting in $j \times j = j^2$ which as shown above is equal to -1. This conforms nicely with normal graphical work in which values on the x-axis to the right of the y-axis are positive whereas values to the left are negative. A further multiplication by j brings us again to the imaginary axis but now below the real axis so that $-1 \times j = -j$. Just one more 90° move anti-clockwise reaches the reference axis with $-j \times j = (-j^2) = 1$.

In Figure 8.1(ii) suppose that we wish to express the points P and Q in complex notation. From P and Q dotted lines may be drawn to meet the real and imaginary axes as shown so that the position of P on this particular scale is quoted as $(4 + j3)$, the 4 is real and the 3 imaginary. The position of Q is $(-2 - j5)$, i.e. $-(2 + j5)$.

This is quoting the positions of P and Q in complex notation. However we may prefer to know the value of the *modulus* of the impedance which is given by the magnitude of, for example, OP together with the angle it makes with the reference axis, known as th *argument*. The modulus and argument together are known as the *polar coordinates* and change from complex to polar is quite simple. Once again from Pythagoras and using the example above we calculate the lengths of the phasors OP and

154

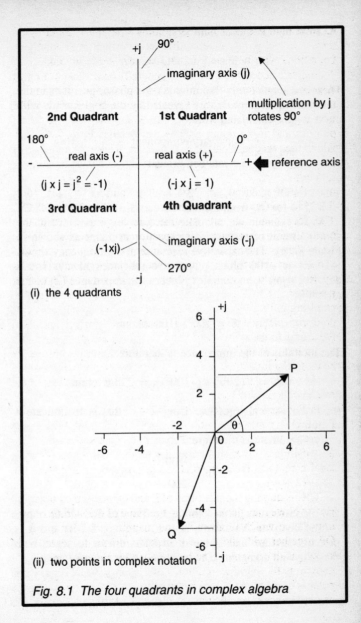

+j 90°

imaginary axis (j)

multiplication by j
rotates 90°

2nd Quadrant   **1st Quadrant**

180°

real axis (-)   real axis (+)   0°

$+$ ◀ reference axis

$(j \times j = j^2 = -1)$ $(-j \times j = 1)$

3rd Quadrant   **4th Quadrant**

imaginary axis (-j)

$(-1 \times j)$

270°

-j

(i) the 4 quadrants

(ii) two points in complex notation

Fig. 8.1 The four quadrants in complex algebra

OQ from their complex numbers:

$$OP = \sqrt{(4^2 + 3^2)} = 5 \qquad OQ = \sqrt{(2^2 + 5^2)} = 5.4$$

These are lengths only (the moduli), the phasor positions in the quadrant (the arguments) are revealed by the angles made with the real axis, calculated from:

$$\tan \theta = \frac{\text{imaginary component}}{\text{real component}}$$

which for OP makes θ, $\tan^{-1} 3/4 = 36.9°$ and for OQ, $\tan^{-1} 5/2 = 68.2°$ or for OQ from the reference axis, $180 + 68.2 = 248.2°$.

As an example we calculate the complex impedance of the simple circuit of resistor and capacitor in series as shown in Figure 8.2(i). The capacitive reactance at the frequency shown $(-1/\omega C)$ is -100 ohms (capacitive reactance always has a negative sign) so in complex algebra the impedance (Z) of the circuit is:

$$Z = 200 - j100 \text{ ohms.}$$

The modulus of the impedance is therefore:

$$|Z| = \sqrt{\{200^2 + (-100^2)\}} = 223.6 \text{ ohms}$$

(note the vertical lines enclosing Z – this is to indicate a modulus).

The argument is therefore:

$$\theta = \tan^{-1} \frac{-100}{200} = -26.6°$$

and the impedance is therefore quoted as $223.6 \angle -26.6°$ ohms.

The complex diagram is shown in Figure 8.2(ii) and it is perhaps obvious that if the diagram is drawn to scale, both modulus and argument may be obtained by measurement.

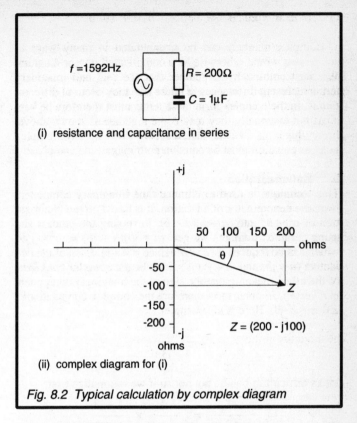

(i) resistance and capacitance in series

Z = (200 - j100) ohms

(ii) complex diagram for (i)

Fig. 8.2 Typical calculation by complex diagram

8.1.1 Changing Between Complex and Polar Forms

We have already made such a change above in order to appreciate that an impedance can be stated in two different ways. A polar form is simply expressed by $r \angle \theta$ (or $Z \angle \theta$) in which r is the magnitude of the vector {e.g. OP in Fig. 8.1(ii)} and θ is the angle made with the reference axis. Hence if a complex expression is stated as $(a + jb)$, then as already shown, it can be changed to the polar form for:

$$r \angle \theta = \sqrt{(a^2 + b^2)} \tan^{-1} b/a$$

Changing from polar to complex follows:

$$a = r \cos \theta \qquad\qquad b = r \sin \theta.$$

Complex numbers can be manipulated in many ways to solve what would otherwise be a complicated phasor diagram. We must continually remember that the real and imaginary terms represent differences in phase (i.e. they occur at different *times*). In the complex form these terms must therefore be kept apart but eventually they may come together as shown above. From this it is evident that the two sides of any complex number equation must be equal in both magnitude and phase.

8.2 Rationalization

This technique is used to eliminate the imaginary component from the denominator of a fraction. It is based on the factorization of $a^2 - b^2$ into $(a + b)(a - b)$. Reversing the process and using complex numbers we get $(a + jb)(a - jb) = a^2 - j^2b^2$ which can be reduced to $a^2 + b^2$ (since $j^2 = -1$). Each of the two factors $(a + jb)$ and $(a - jb)$ is said to be the *complex conjugate* of the other, meaning that the sign of the imaginary component is reversed. In polar form therefore the complex conjugate of $r \angle\theta$ is $r \angle-\theta$. Here is an example:

$$\frac{1}{4 - j3}$$

looks difficult to handle but not so if we rationalize first:

$$\frac{1}{4 - j3} = \frac{1}{4 - j3} \times \frac{4 + j3}{4 + j3}$$

here the numerator and denominator are both multiplied by the complex conjugate, hence:

$$\frac{4 + j3}{4^2 + 3^2} = \frac{4 + j3}{25} = 0.16 + j\,0.12.$$

If the denominator contains a j term only then we simply multiply both numerator and denominator by j.

8.3 Addition and Subtraction of Complex Numbers

No problem here provided that we remember that there is a *time* difference between real and imaginary parts and therefore these must always be kept separate. Hence to add two complex numbers we simply add the real parts and then add the imaginary parts, similary with subtraction. Thus for two phasors $(a + jb)$ and $(c + jd)$:

$$(a + jb) + (c + jd) = (a + c) + j(b + d)$$

or with subtraction :

$$(a + jb) - (c + jd) = (a - c) + j(b - d)$$

Here is an example to really test our complex algebra skills. For the circuit of Figure 8.3(i) calculate the current I and its time relationship with the voltage. We choose a frequency f of 1592Hz for which the number of radians per second (ω) is $2\pi f = 10^4$.

Reactance of the inductance, L is ωL which is 15 ohms. Then for path 1 the impedance Z_1 is $R_1 + j\omega L = 8 + j15$ ohms. Hence the current

$$I_1 = \frac{V}{Z_1} = \frac{100}{8 + j15}$$

which by rationalizing (Sect.8.2) gives:

$$\frac{800 - j1500}{8^2 + 15^2}$$

i.e. $2.77 - j5.19$ amperes as shown in the 4th quadrant in (ii) of the Figure.

Again, reactance of the capacitor C is $-1/\omega C$ which is -5 ohms, so for path 2, the impedance Z_2 is $R_2 - j/\omega C = 12 - j5$ ohms, hence the current

$$I_2 = \frac{V}{Z_2} = \frac{100}{12 - j5}$$

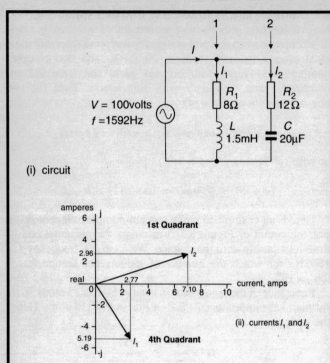

(i) circuit

(ii) currents I_1 and I_2

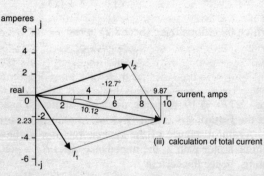

(iii) calculation of total current

Fig.8.3   Complex features of a parallel circuit

which after rationalizing gives 7.10 + j2.96 amperes as shown in the first quadrant in the Figure.

By combining these two currents (I_1 and I_2) we can calculate the total current I which is obtained by completing the parallelogram of sides I_1 and I_2 and drawing the diagonal, hence:

$$I = (2.77 - j5.19) + (7.10 + j2.96)$$

and adding real and imaginary components separately we get:

$$I = 9.87 - j2.23 \text{ amperes}$$

as shown in (iii) of the Figure.

We can put this into polar form:

$$I = \sqrt{(9.87^2 + 2.23^2)} \ \tan^{-1} \frac{-2.23}{9.87} = 10.12 \ \angle -12.7° \text{ amperes.}$$

The wave period $T = 1/f = 1/1592$ seconds so because I lags 12.7° on V, I reaches any point in the cycle:

$$\frac{1}{1592} \times \frac{12.7}{360} \times 10^6 \text{ microseconds (μs) ,}$$

i.e. just over 22 μs later than does the voltage.

We see from this example that addition and subtraction of phasors can only be carried out with cartesian coordinates, hence the especial use of complex algebra. It is also evident from the example why real and imaginary parts must be kept apart for here the fact that there is a time difference between voltage and current is clearly indicated.

8.4 Multiplication and Division of Complex Numbers

If $(a + jb)$ and $(c + jd)$ are two phasors to be multiplied together, then :

$$(a + jb)(c + jd) + ac + jad + jbc + j^2bd$$

and remembering that real and imaginary parts must be kept apart, also that $j^2 = -1$:

$$(a + jb)(c + jd) = (ac - bd) + j(ad + bc).$$

For division one stage of rationalization is involved :

$$\frac{(a + jb)}{(c + jd)} = \frac{(a + jb)(c - jd)}{c^2 + d^2} = \frac{(ac + bd) + j(bc - ad)}{c^2 + d^2}$$

It is generally found however that multiplication and division are less complicated when using the polar forms, it is in fact easier to see what the result means :

Multiplication: $\quad r_1 \angle\theta_1 \times r_2 \angle\theta_2 = r_1 r_2 \angle(\theta_1 + \theta_2)$,

i.e. the moduli are multiplied and the angles are added.

Division: $\quad \dfrac{r_1 \angle\theta_1}{r_2 \angle\theta_2} = \dfrac{r_1}{r_2} \angle(\theta_1 - \theta_2)$,

i.e. the moduli are divided and the angles are subtracted.

In the following example we find the modulus and angle of the complex expression:

$$\frac{4 - j3}{2 + j}$$

Modulus of numerator $\quad = \sqrt{(4^2 + 3^2)} = 5$

Modulus of denominator $\quad = \sqrt{(2^2 + 1^2)} = \sqrt{5}$

Modulus of expression $\quad = \dfrac{5}{\sqrt{5}} = \dfrac{5\sqrt{5}}{\sqrt{5} \times \sqrt{5}} = \sqrt{5}$

Angle of numerator $\quad = \tan^{-1} -3/4 = -36.87°$

Angle of denominator $\quad = \tan^{-1} 1/2 = 26.57°$

$\therefore$ Angle of expression $\quad = -36.87° - 26.57° = -63.44°$

Hence the complex fraction

$$\frac{4 - j3}{2 + j}$$

may be expressed in polar notation as $\sqrt{5} \angle -63.44°$.

Chapter 9

STATISTICAL ANALYSIS

In a few words statistics are concerned with the scientific collection, classification and analysis of numerical data. The technique began in the 17th Century with the mathematical studies mainly by the Frenchman, Blaise Pascal and the Italian astronomer, Gallileo, these studies then being mainly of gambling. Much of statistical analysis has been developed to keep within bounds the uncontrollable element of *chance* which unfortunately always plays tricks on us. Probability theory was therefore born out of games of chance and we can hardly escape the gambling element controlling each of us daily, from relying on the alarm clock to wake us on time to crossing the road later. By use of modern statistical techniques, sensible conclusions can be drawn and through probability calculations predictions are possible, but not without an element of uncertainty. Accordingly this chapter is about the conclusions we are entitled to reach when provided with certain facts and figures. One conclusion we might reach is that every question of life or death (including our own) remains a probability until we know the outcome.

9.1 Frequency
"Frequency" in statistics has a slightly different meaning from what it has in electronics. In electronics it is the number of repetitions in a stated *time* (usually one second). In statistics however it may be defined as the ratio of the number of actual to the number of possible occurrences of an event. We therefore see that in statistics time is of no concern.

Let us plunge straight into an electronics manufacturing problem which is that of analysing the factory output of 1 000 ± 2% ohm resistors. The question of course is whether all of the resistors fall within the ± 2% range and how the values are distributed. The figures are said to represent a *sample* of the *population* (i.e. the total number). From the figures of this sample, reasonable predictions can be made about the whole batch.

Sample of 60 x 1 000 ohm Resistors (ohms):

```
1009  987  1014  986  995  1005  998  1006  1001  1011  996  1008  990  1000  1023
1000  1003  999  979  995  1028  1012  1011  987  991  1006  1007  993   994  1001
1017  984  1003  991  987  1015  985  1003  998  983  1013  997  990  1004  1002
974  1008  1015  995  993  1001  1002  991  975  985  981  981  997   989  997
```

As in mathematics generally, the Greek capital sigma, Σ, is used as shorthand for "the sum of" and if x is used as a general symbol for the value of any given item in the sample, then Σx represents the sum of all the individual values. Let there be n of these. Several types of calculation can be made on these figures. Possibly the simplest is the *mean* (or average) which is simply the sum of all the values divided by their number, i.e. $\Sigma x/n$. The mean of the sample (usually denoted by $\bar{x}$) is unlikely to be the same as that of the population, only an estimate of it. For the figures given above, $n = 60$, $\Sigma x = 59\ 891$, sample mean = 998.18.

The mean is one way of representing a whole set by a single figure. Although frequently used, it can lead to wrong conclusions for considering, as a simple example, the two sets of figures, 8,9,10 and 3,7,11,15, both have a mean of 9 yet clearly the sets differ widely. See the example in Section 9.2 for how we cope with this.

Such calculations are useful to the expert but perhaps the most illustrative is the *histogram* in which the frequency of occurrence is plotted vertically with the various ranges of values marked horizontally. Such a histogram is shown in Figure 9.1 for our batch of 60 resistors (ignore the probability scale at this stage). Before the histogram can be drawn, a *frequency of occurrence* table is constructed by grouping the data into a number of equal *class intervals* (in this case resistance ranges) and the frequency or number of times that values occur within each interval is recorded as shown below. There is little doubt that such a pictorial representation as in the Figure tells more than a batch of figures.

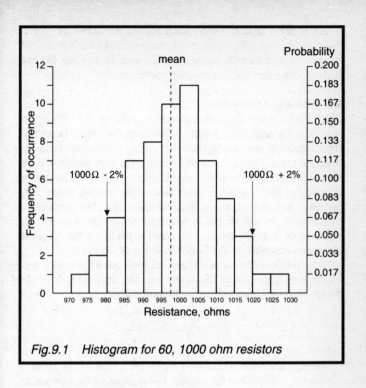

Fig.9.1   Histogram for 60, 1000 ohm resistors

Distribution of Resistance Values :

Class Intervals	Frequency
970–974	1
975–979	2
980–984	4
985–989	7
990–994	8
995–999	10
1000–1004	11
1005–1009	7
1010–1014	5
1015–1019	3
1020–1024	1
1025–1029	1

An immediate conclusion from Figure 9.1 is that not all of the resistors are within the ± 2% range. This of course could have been read directly from the resistance figures but the histogram illustrates the discrepancy more clearly.

9.2 Standard Deviation

This is a measure of *dispersion* (or *variability*), i.e. the extent to which the individual values differ from the mean. In assessing dispersion we cannot take the average deviation from the mean because the result would be zero – the very position of the mean is such that the positive deviations cancel the negative. Averaging the squares of the deviations makes everything positive and so removes this complication but because a measure of the deviations is required, not of the squares, the square root is finally taken. The result of all this is the *standard deviation*, denoted by the Greek lower case sigma, σ.

The standard deviation is therefore defined as the square root of the average value of the squares of the deviations from the mean of the original values, mathematically:

$$\sigma = \sqrt{\frac{\Sigma (x - \overline{x})^2}{n}}$$

Here is a simple illustration based on the example given in Section 9.1. Calculate the standard deviations of the two sets of figures 8,9,10 and 3,7,11,15. As shown previously, both sets have a mean of 9.

Set 1 :

Numbers	Deviation from mean $(x - \overline{x})$	(Deviations)^2 $(x - \overline{x})^2$
8	−1	1
9	0	0
10	+1	1

$$n = 3, \quad \Sigma(x - \overline{x})^2 = 2,$$

hence standard deviation, $\sigma = \sqrt{(2/3)} = 0.82$

Set 2 :

3	–6	36
7	–2	4
11	+2	4
15	+6	36

$$n = 4, \quad \Sigma(x - \overline{x})^2 = 80$$

hence standard deviation, $\sigma = \sqrt{(80/4)} = 4.47$.

Clearly, although both sets have a mean of 9, calculation of the standard deviation shows how different the two sets are by the dispersion.

For readers with sufficient patience and a scientific calculator or computer to match, the standard deviation for the 60 resistors of Section 9.1 is 11.55 ohms.

9.3 Probability

Everyday conversation uses probability, for example "it is unlikely to rain today" is our way of saying that the probability of rain arriving is small. In statistics we cannot tolerate such loose thinking hence a scale of measurement is required. Accordingly probability is defined as the extent to which an event is likely to occur and it is expressed by the ratio of the number of cases likely to happen to the full number possible. Probability is therefore the essence of *prediction*, it enables us to assign a number to the possibility of an event happening. Prediction must involve some uncertainty, however the aim of statistical techniques is to minimize this.

The probability scale runs from 0 to 1, 0 for the impossibility of an event occurring, 1 for certainty. Most practical events have probabilities somewhere in between.

As a simple example, a coin tossed properly (i.e. with no bias) is as likely to produce a head as a tail. Generally we use the letter n to represent the total number of possible results with m for the number of successful ones. Denoting the probability that an event E will happen by P_E, then $P_E = m/n$, hence for tossing a coin:

$$n = 2, \quad m = 1$$

hence the probability of a head, $P_H = 0.5$ and that of a tail, $P_T = 0.5$.

$$P_H + P_T = 0.5 + 0.5 = 1 ,$$

which shows the certainty of either a head or a tail.

Also throwing a dice, $n = 6$, $m = 1$, hence $P_1 = 1/6$, $P_2 = 1/6$, $P_5 = 1/6$, etc.

For the gamblers among us, the roulette wheel has 37 numbers $(0 - 36)$, the probability of any one coming up is low at 1 in 37, i.e. 0.027.

9.3.1 Probability Distributions

From Figure 9.1 we now take as an example the range of resistance values $1\,000 - 1\,005$. There is a total of 60 measurements and 11 are contained in this range. The probability of any resistor having a value in this range is therefore 11 in 60, i.e. 0.183. The calculation is similar for each of the other ranges and the probability range is marked on the scale on the right. With this scale the Figure is now that of a *probability distribution* and we see that the probability scale is the frequency scale divided by the total number of items, n.

From this it is possible to calculate the probability of a resistor being outside the stated range of $1\,000 \pm 2\%$.

From the Figure, the probability of a resistor having a resistance within the range:

970 – 975 is 0.017		975 – 980 is 0.033
1020 – 1025 is 0.017		1025 – 1030 is 0.017

The probability of any resistor being outside the 2% limits is the sum of these, i.e. 0.084, this may appear to be low but it does indicate that there could be 84 resistors in every batch of 1000 outside of the tolerance limits. Of interest also is the fact that the probability of *not* being outside of the limits is $1-0.084 = 0.916$.

9.3.2 *Normal Distribution Curves*

In Figure 9.1 the steps in the histogram are wide simply because we chose measurements to the nearest 5 ohms. By choosing say, 1 ohm intervals instead, it is evident that the steps in the histogram would become less pronounced and in fact the histogram itself would then tend towards a smooth curve simply because the number of bars would be multiplied by 5 with each bar one fifth of the width. It is evident that by reducing the width of the steps still further, the histogram becomes more nearly a smooth curve.

So far we have only considered a relatively small sample of resistors, a larger one would therefore have had better predictive powers. By testing all the items we would then obviously obtain the true answer but this is exactly what we are trying to avoid because of the amount of work involved. It is possible however to calculate and draw a theoretical predictive curve from the results of a small sample such as in Figure 9.1. Karl Friedrich Gauss in the early 1800's was one of the first mathematicians to study how curves can be fitted to histograms. A most useful *Gaussian curve* is the *Normal Distribution Curve* for it seems to suit many investigations.

Firstly let us see how useful a normal distribution curve can be. Figure 9.2(i) shows a typical curve which is a probability distribution of the height of men from a certain country. An area has been shaded for men between 165 and 175 cm height. This area represents the probability that a man selected at random will have a height between these figures. We can also look at this as that the percentage of the population (of these men) in this range is indicated by expressing the shaded area as a percentage of the total area under the curve.

All very well but for a start we do not know the mathematical equation to the curve so such calculations do not seem possible. Happily as mentioned above, for many purposes the normal distribution curve conforms to what is required and what is more, it can be produced from two measurements only, the mean and standard deviation (Sects. 9.1 and 9.2) of the population which are estimated from the sample. Figure 9.2(ii) shows the outline of the histogram of Figure 9.1(i) with the appropriate Gaussian distribution curve added. This is a smooth curve which, derived only from measurements on the sample,

171

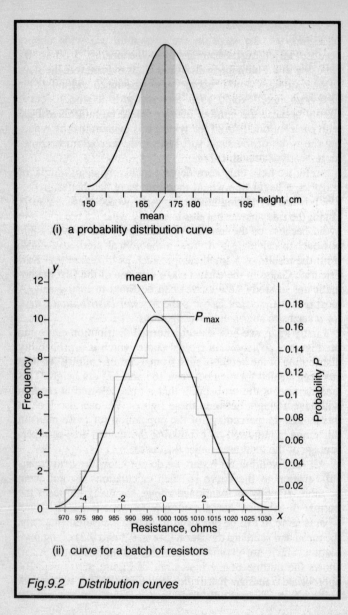

(i) a probability distribution curve

(ii) curve for a batch of resistors

Fig.9.2   Distribution curves

172

predicts the probability of the various values arising in the total population.

The appropriate mathematical equation published by Gauss is frightening enough but it can lead to a simple method of sketching the curve based only on the mean and standard deviation as mentioned above. In this example the mean is 998.18 ohms and the standard deviation for an interval of one ohm is $11.5/5 = 2.3$. The full equation is :

$$\text{probability} = \frac{1}{\sigma\sqrt{2\pi}} \times e^{(-x)/(2\sigma)}$$

where x is in terms of standard deviations (s.d.'s.). The curve of Figure 9.2(ii) is calculated from this formula.

A simplified method of developing the curve has been developed, it is based on the fact that as shown above, the curve can be defined by two parameters only (mean and s.d.). As seen from Figure 9.2(ii) the maximum probability P_{max} occurs at the mean and from the formula it has a value :

$$P_{max} = \frac{1}{\sigma\sqrt{2\pi}} \quad \text{i.e.} \quad \frac{0.3989}{2.3} = 0.173$$

Now it is possible to work in terms of standard deviations, the results of which are:

for 1 s.d. from the mean,

$$P_1 = P_{max} \times e^{-0.5} = P_{max} \times 0.6065 = 0.105$$

for 2 s.d.'s from the mean,

$$P_2 = P_{max} \times e^{-2} = P_{max} \times 0.135 = 0.023$$

for 3 s.d.'s from the mean,

$$P_3 = P_{max} \times e^{-4.5} = P_{max} \times 0.011 = 0.002$$

so giving just enough points for sketching in the curve. More points can be calculated if desired.

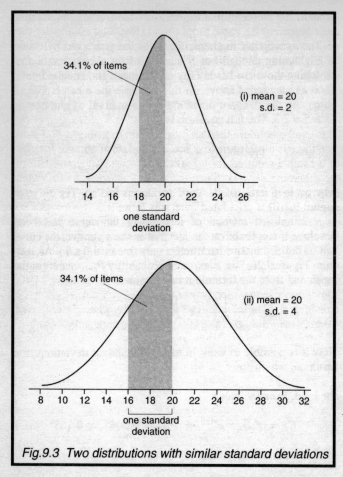

34.1% of items

(i) mean = 20
s.d. = 2

14   16   18   20   22   24   26

one standard
deviation

34.1% of items

(ii) mean = 20
s.d. = 4

8   10   12   14   16   18   20   22   24   26   28   30   32

one standard
deviation

Fig.9.3 Two distributions with similar standard deviations

Another most interesting and useful feature of the normal distribution curve is that irrespective of the values of the mean and standard deviation, that proportion of the total population which occurs between the mean and a specified number of standard deviations away from it, is constant. This is shown pictorially in Figure 9.3(i) and (ii), showing two completely different distributions {there is more dispersion in (ii)}. Each is shown with a shaded area extending over, for example, one standard deviation from the mean. In both cases the shaded areas represent the same proportion of the total area under the curve. Accordingly in (i) 34.1% of the items are likely to fall within the range 18–20 and because of the symmetry of the curve, also from 20–22. In (ii) the ranges are 16–20 and 20–24.

* * * * *

This can be no more than an introduction to a very useful subject, there is much more to come, e.g. the calculation of the size of a sample required for a realistic forecast, yet derived from the minimum of work. Then there are *confidence limits* which help us to quote results with greater precision, e.g for the normal distribution 95% of the population lies within ± 1.96 standard deviations from the mean. This is equivalent to saying that there is a probability of 0.95 that the characteristics of any item taken at random from the population will lie within this range. So far also we have considered problems containing a single variable, e.g. resistance values, heights of men. Many situations arise in which two or even more variables have to be considered. These are catered for by *Regression and Correlation*. Statistics is truly an all-embracing subject.

Chapter 10

INTRODUCTION TO CALCULUS

Calculus would have been a welcome addition to Archimedes' repertoire for even his continuing struggles to determine the ratio between the circumference of a circle and its diameter led only to a moderately accurate result. Calculus is the study of the rate at which quantities change. The word has been borrowed from Latin and originally referred to a small stone used for reckoning on an abacus. The technique was successfully developed following the work of both Newton and Leibnitz in the 17th Century. The study can be broadly divided into two parts, *differential calculus* which is concerned with the ratio of small differences and *integral calculus* which is the inverse of this –all very mysterious until we see the ideas in action.

This is a subject which normally warrants a king-size volume on its own, evidently here we can do no more than begin to understand its purpose and how it functions.

10.1 Differential Calculus

Take any graph, say of the distance an object moves against the time taken. If the graph is a straight line, the indication is that the velocity of the object is constant, if on the other hand, the graph is a curve, the velocity is varying. A curve cannot be handled in the same way as a straight line because its *slope* which indicates the velocity at any instant, is constantly changing. This is the type of problem in which differential calculus reigns supreme. Expressed more precisely, differential calculus deals with the *rate of change* of a function. As we well know, the rate of change of distance with time is the velocity, similarly the rate of change of velocity is the acceleration. These are just two examples of rate of change.

Put more mathematically, if $y = f(x)$ (y is a function of x), the method tells us how much y will increase or decrease if x changes slightly.

We can illustrate this graphically as in Figure 10.1 for if the curve $y = f(x)$ is drawn, the rate of change of y is proportional to the slope of the curve. For a curve such as shown, it is clear that the slope or rate of change varies and it is important that the changes we consider are small otherwise a true idea of the slope of the curve at the point in question cannot be obtained.

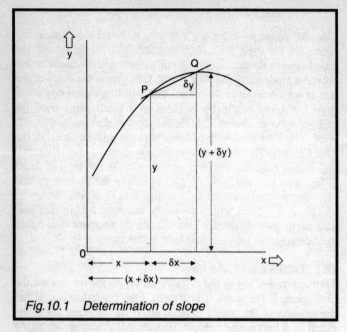

Fig.10.1   Determination of slope

Small changes in the values of for example, x and y are usually denoted by δx and δy (δ is the Greek *delta*) and the rate of change at any point on the curve is the ratio of the increases in y and x, i.e. by

$$\frac{\delta y}{\delta x}.$$

In the Figure we wish to find the slope of the curve at P which has coordinates x, y. To illustrate the technique an adjacent point Q is required which as shown, has coordinates $x + \delta x$ and $y + \delta y$. Then the ratio $\delta y/\delta x$ gives the slope of the line PQ. By moving Q towards P, both δy and δx decrease and ultimately as Q moves up closely to P, δy and δx both approach zero and the ratio $\delta y/\delta x$ approaches some finite value which in fact is the slope of the curve at P. This value is denoted by dy/dx. In other words :

$$\frac{dy}{dx} \text{ is the limit of the ratio } \frac{\delta y}{\delta x}$$

as δx (and therefore also δy) approach zero, i.e.

$$\frac{dy}{dx} = \lim_{\delta x \to 0} \frac{\delta y}{\delta x}$$

Hence dy/dx expresses the rate of change of y (the slope) at the point P (x,y).

We can again express this in words by saying that the limit of the ratio of the increment of y to the increment of x when the latter increment is made zero, is known as the "differential coefficient of y with respect to x" (dy/dx).

Just a reminder here – never forget that for example, δx means "a small change in x", it cannot be split up into δ and x.

10.1.1 Differentiation of Some Particular Functions

Let us put the above into practice by finding dy/dx when

$$y = 9 + 4x + 3x^2 \qquad \text{....(1)}$$

We first find what happens when y is increased slightly, i.e. to $y + \delta y$:

$$y + \delta y = 9 + 4(x + \delta x) + 3(x + \delta x)^2$$

$$= 9 + 4x + 4\delta x + 3x^2 + 6x\delta x + 3(\delta x)^2 \qquad \text{....(2)}$$

Next subtract (1) from (2) :

$$\delta y = 4\delta x + 6x\delta x + 3(\delta x)^2$$

and dividing through by δx :

$$\frac{\delta y}{\delta x} = 4 + 6x + 3\delta x$$

Now when $\delta x = 0$, $\delta y/\delta x$ becomes dy/dx, hence for $\delta x = 0$

$$\frac{dy}{dx} = 4 + 6x$$

We do not normally have to go through this procedure line by line, general rules for quick differentiation follow later.

This can be considered more critically by seeing what happens to $\delta y/\delta x$ as x approaches any value, say, 2.0

When

$$x = 2, \quad y = 9 + 4x + 3x^2 = 29$$

and

$$\frac{dy}{dx} = 4 + 6x = 16$$

x	2.05	2.02	2.01	2.001	1.999
y	29.8075	29.3212	29.1603	29.016	28.984
δx	0.05	0.02	0.01	0.001	–0.001
δy	0.8075	0.3212	0.1603	0.016	–0.016
$\delta y/\delta x$	16.15	16.06	16.03	16.00	16.00

Clearly here $\delta y/\delta x$ approaches 16 as x approaches the value of 2, hence when $x = 2$, as we have found above, $dy/dx = 4 + 6x = 16$.

Note that the constant value of 9 in the equation for y has disappeared on differentiation. Constants are always rejected in this way because they do not affect the *slope* or shape of a curve, they only raise or lower it.

Next we differentiate

$$y = ax^3 \qquad \qquad ....(1).$$

Using the method shown above:

$$(y + \delta y) = a(x + \delta x)^3 \qquad \qquad ....(2)$$

180

Subtracting (1) from (2) :

$$\delta y = a(x + \delta x)^3 - ax^3$$

$$= a(x^3 + 3x^2\delta x + 3x\delta x^2 + \delta x^3) - ax^3$$

$$= 3ax^2\delta x + 3ax\delta x^2 + a\delta x^3$$

and dividing through by δx :

$$\frac{\delta y}{\delta x} = 3ax^2 + 3ax\delta x + a\delta x^2$$

Now when $\delta x = 0$,

$$\frac{\delta y}{\delta x} \quad \text{becomes} \quad \frac{dy}{dx}$$

hence for $\delta x = 0$:

$$\frac{dy}{dx} = 3ax^2$$

Now comes a rule for quick differentiation of say, x^n

$$\frac{dy}{dx} \quad \text{for} \quad x^n = nx^{n-1}$$

and this is important. The index becomes a multiplier of the expression and a new index is created of 1 less. Thus as above

for $\qquad y = ax^3, \quad \dfrac{dy}{dx} = 3ax^2$

Again for $\quad y = 3x^3 + 8x = 3x^3 + 8x^1, \quad \dfrac{dy}{dx} = 9x^2 + 8$

(for $x^0 = 1$).

Also remenbering that constants disappear:

for $\qquad y = 5x^2 - 4x + 7, \quad \dfrac{dy}{dx} = 10x - 4$

181

Even finding the differential coefficient of $y = 1/x^2$ is straight-forward :

for $\quad 1/x^2 = x^{-2}\quad$ hence $\quad \dfrac{dy}{dx} = -2x^{-3}\quad$ or $\quad \dfrac{-2}{x^3}$

* * * * *

We should by now have sufficient experience of the basic techniques involved to appreciate the general expression for defining a differential coefficient. Generally we say that y is some function of x or:

$$y = f(x)$$
.....(i)

and because $(y + \delta y)$ and $(x + \delta x)$ are simultaneous values, then :

$$(y + \delta y) = f(x + \delta x)$$
.....(ii)

On subtracting (i) from (ii) –

$$\delta y = f(x + \delta x) - f(x)$$
.....(iii)

Now from Section 10.1

$$\frac{dy}{dx} = \lim_{\delta x \to 0} \frac{\delta y}{\delta x}$$

hence:

$$\frac{dy}{dx} = \lim_{\delta x \to 0} \frac{f(x + \delta x) - f(x)}{\delta x}$$
.....(iv)

this in fact is the basic formula from which derivatives are calculated.

Here is the formula in use to find the slope of the curve $y = x^2$ at the point x, y.

Then $f(x) = x^2$ and:

$$\frac{\delta y}{\delta x} = \frac{(x + \delta x)^2 - x^2}{\delta x} = \frac{x^2 + 2x\delta x + \delta x^2 - x^2}{\delta x} =$$

$$= \frac{2x\delta x + \delta x^2}{\delta x} = 2x + \delta x$$

Now dy/dx is the limit of this when $\delta x = 0$

$$\therefore \qquad \frac{dy}{dx} = 2x$$

showing that the slope of the curve at any point is equal to $2x$, e.g. at the point $x = 5$, $y = 25$, the slope is 10. We can look at this in figures because :

$$\text{at } x = 4.5, \quad y = 20.25$$
$$\text{at } x = 5.5, \quad y = 30.25$$

showing that the increase in 1 for x over the centre point $x = 5$ results in an increase in y of 10.

Next consider the transistor input characteristic shown in Figure 10.2. We wish to calculate the a.c. resistance (not the d.c. resistance which is simply V_{BE}/I_B) at the point P (i.e. at 1 V) – not an easy task but we now have calculus to help us.

Firstly it is necessary to find the equation to the curve and it is a fact that many transistor input curves conform reasonably well to the equation $I = kV^n$. One way of seeing whether the curve of Figure 10.2 can be expressed by such an equation is by calculating the values of the constants k and n at the two ends of the curve and then using the results to calculate a point in the middle. Points near the ends of the curve:

$$\text{at } V_{BE} = 0.5 \text{ V}, \qquad I_B = 0.1 \text{ mA}$$

$$\text{at } V_{BE} = 1.2 \text{ V}, \qquad I_B = 2.0 \text{ mA}$$

We need not bring I_B to amperes provided that account of this is taken finally. Then:

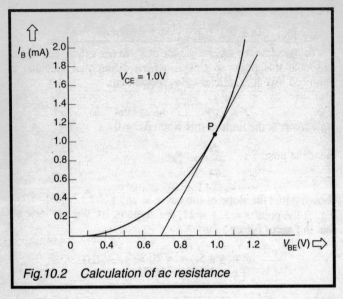

Fig.10.2   Calculation of ac resistance

$$0.1 = k \times 0.5^n \qquad \qquad ....(i)$$

$$2.0 = k \times 1.2^n \qquad \qquad ....(ii)$$

and by taking logarithms of both sides of each equation, then subtracting (i) from (ii) :

$$
\begin{array}{rl}
0.3010 = & \log k + 0.0792\,n \\
-1.0 \quad = & \log k - 0.3010\,n \\
\hline
1.3010 = & \qquad\quad 0.3802\,n
\end{array}
$$

from which $n \approx 3.42$ and by substituting for n in either of the above equations, $k = 1.07$. Hence a possible equation to the curve is:

$$I_B = 1.07\,V_{BE}^{3.42}\ \text{mA}.$$

By checking at $V_{BE} = 1.0$ V (point P),

184

$$I_B = 1.07 \times 1.0^{3.42} = 1.07$$

which is seen to agree well with Figure 10.2.

To calculate the a.c. resistance at P we need the slope of the curve at this point so this is where differential calculus is required. We have already discovered that:

for $\qquad I = kV^n, \quad \dfrac{dI}{dV} = nkV^{n-1}$

hence at point P :

$$\frac{dI}{dV} = 3.42 \times 1.07 \times 1.0^{2.42}$$

but this is for I in mA, hence for I in amperes:

$$\frac{dI}{dV} = 3.42 \times \frac{1.07}{1000} \times 1.0^{2.42} = 0.003659.$$

(note that $1.0^{2.42} = 1$).

The a.c. resistance is derived from the reciprocal of the slope, i.e.

$$\frac{1}{0.003659} = 273 \text{ ohms.}$$

Differential Coefficient of e^x :
Using the quick method of differentiation outlined above, we start from the series for e^x as given in Section 7.4:

$$e^x = 1 + x + \frac{x^2}{2!} + \frac{x^3}{3!} + \frac{x^4}{4!} + \ldots\ldots\ldots$$

$$\therefore \quad \frac{dy}{dx}(e^x) = 0 + 1 + \frac{2x^1}{2} + \frac{3x^2}{3 \times 2} + \frac{4x^3}{4 \times 3 \times 2} + \ldots\ldots\ldots$$

$$= 1 + x + \frac{x^2}{2!} + \frac{x^3}{3!} + \frac{x^4}{4!} + \ldots\ldots\ldots$$

185

and it is immediately evident that the series obtained by differentiation is exactly the same as the original series, i.e.:

$$\frac{dy}{dx}(e^x) = e^x .$$

10.1.2 Products and Quotients

Here we skip the proofs and simply quote the results.

Products:
for $y = f(x) = u \times v$ where u and v are both functions of x:

$$\frac{dy}{dx} = u \cdot \frac{dv}{dx} + v \cdot \frac{du}{dx}$$

As a simple example, we calculate dy/dx for the expression $(x^2 + 4)(3x - 1)$ by splitting y into two products where $u = (x^2 + 4)$ and $v = (3x - 1)$.

$$\frac{dy}{dx} = (x^2 + 4) \times 3 + (3x - 1) \times 2x$$

$$= 3x^2 + 12 + 6x^2 - 2x = 9x^2 - 2x + 12$$

Let us now check by using the quick differentiation method shown above:

$$y = (x^2 + 4)(3x - 1) = 3x^3 - x^2 + 12x - 4$$

$$\therefore \quad \frac{dy}{dx} = 9x^2 - 2x + 12$$

Quotients:
this gets slightly more complicated and in this case it may be shown that if $y = f(x) = u/v$, where u and v are both functions of x :

$$\frac{dy}{dx} = \frac{v\dfrac{du}{dx} - u\dfrac{dv}{dx}}{v^2}$$

Let us calculate dy/dx for the expression $\{(x^2 + 4)/(3x - 1)\}$, here $u = (x^2 + 4)$ and $v = (3x - 1)$.

$$\frac{dy}{dx} = \frac{(3x - 1) \times 2x - (x^2 + 4) \times 3}{(3x - 1)^2} =$$

$$= \frac{6x^2 - 2x - 3x^2 - 12}{(3x - 1)^2} =$$

$$= \frac{3x^2 - 2x - 12}{(3x - 1)^2}.$$

10.1.3 *Trigonometrical Functions*
Using the general method of determining the differential coefficient as outlined in Section 10.1.1, let us now consider $f(x) = \sin x$, then:

$$\frac{dy}{dx} = \lim_{\delta x \to 0} \frac{f(x + \delta x) - f(x)}{\delta x}$$

$$= \lim_{\delta x \to 0} \frac{\sin (x + dx) - \sin x}{\delta x}$$

$$= \lim_{\delta x \to 0} \frac{\sin x \cdot \cos \delta x + \cos x \cdot \sin \delta x - \sin x}{\delta x}$$

(see Sect.6.3.1 for expansion of $\sin (x + \delta x)$.

Now it can be shown directly from natural sine tables or by reasoning from the fact that when the angle in a right-angled triangle is reduced to 0, then the sine of the angle (obtained from the ratio perpendicular/hypotenuse) must be 0 because the length of the perpendicular is 0. It can further be shown that for *small angles* $\sin x$ (and $\tan x$) can be taken as approximately equal to x (in radians). Similarly $\cos x$ is approximately equal to 1. The smaller the angle of course, the more accurate this approximation becomes, e.g. for sines the error is less than 2% for angles up to around 20°.

Summing up: $\sin 0° = 0,\quad \cos 0° = 1.$

Hence as $\delta x \to 0$, $\cos \delta x \to 1$ and $\sin \delta x \to \delta x$

hence $\dfrac{d}{dx}(\sin x) = \dfrac{\sin x + \cos x\,\delta x - \sin x}{\delta x} = \cos x$

By using similar reasoning it can be shown that:

$$\frac{d}{dx}(\cos x) = -\sin x$$

The following example uses one more of the many principles involved in calculus, i.e.:

$$\frac{\delta y}{\delta x} = \frac{\delta y}{\delta u} \times \frac{\delta u}{\delta x}$$

and it is evident that however small δy, δx and δu are, as we make them approach 0, each difference ratio approaches its corresponding differential coefficient, i.e.:

$$\frac{dy}{dx} = \frac{dy}{du} \times \frac{du}{dx}$$

The next example embraces one of the well-known formulae concerned with the voltage across an inductance. This as we know, is a function of time because the current flowing through an inductance itself creates a "back e.m.f." which opposes the build-up. A circuit is said to have an inductance (L) of one henry (H) if an e.m.f. of one volt is induced in it when the current is changing at the rate of one ampere per second. Accordingly we let di/dt represent the rate of change of current with time, giving the voltage produced:

$$e = L \times \frac{di}{dt} \quad \text{volts}$$

Consider now an inductor L henries connected in series with a resistance R ohms and let a current i flow through the combination, then the voltage across the series combination is given by:

$$v = iR + L \cdot \frac{di}{dt}$$

Now let $i = I_m \sin \omega t$ where I_m is the maximum current . Then because $d/dx \sin x = \cos x$ (see above):

$$\frac{di}{dt} = I_m \omega \cos \omega t$$

$$\therefore \qquad v = (I_m \sin \omega t)R + (I_m \omega \cos \omega t)L$$

$$= I_m (R \sin \omega t + \omega L \cos \omega t)$$

so here we see that differential calculus has got to grips with an electrical circuit in which the current contains an additional component which changes with time.

The differential coefficient of $\tan x$ follows from the above for if $y = \tan x$, then $y = \sin x/\cos x$. Hence:

$$\frac{dy}{dx} = \frac{\cos x \dfrac{d(\sin x)}{dx} - \sin x \dfrac{d(\cos x)}{dx}}{\cos^2 x}$$

$$= \frac{\cos^2 x + \sin^2 x}{\cos^2 x}$$

Now from Section 6.3, since $\cos^2 x + \sin^2 x = 1$,

$$\frac{dy}{dx} = \frac{1}{\cos^2 x} = \sec^2 x$$

i.e. $$\frac{d}{dx} (\tan x) = \sec^2 x$$

A list of some important derivatives used in trigonometry follows:

y	dy/dx
$\sin x$	$\cos x$
$\sin ax$	$a \cos ax$
$\sin (ax + b)$	$a \cos (ax + b)$
$\cos x$	$-\sin x$
$\cos ax$	$-a \sin ax$
$\cos (ax + b)$	$-a \sin (ax + b)$
$\tan x$	$\sec^2 x$
$\tan ax$	$a \sec^2 ax$
$\cot x$	$-\text{cosec}^2 x$
$\cot ax$	$-a \, \text{cosec}^2 ax$
$\sec x$	$\sec x \cdot \tan x$
$\sec ax$	$a \tan ax \, \sec ax$
$\text{cosec } x$	$-\text{cosec } x \cdot \cot x$
$\text{cosec } ax$	$-a \cot ax \, \text{cosec } ax$
$\cot ax$	$-a \, \text{cosec}^2 ax$

10.1.4 Maximum and Minimum Values

Very useful in electronics is the facility for determining the maximum or minimum values of a function, i.e. when the rate of increase or decrease of its graph is zero. Consider the two graphs in Figure 10.3.

In (i) y is increasing at P as x increases, hence the tangent to the curve is sloping upwards to the right, accordingly dy/dx is said to be positive.

The opposite condition arises in (ii) where y is decreasing at P, the tangent is then sloping downwards to the right and therefore dy/dx is negative.

We look at this in a more practical way in Figure 10.4 which is the graph of $y = 3x^3 - 4x^2 + 5$, hardly one which can be can solved by straightforward algebra, however much information can be gained from a graph. Here $dy/dx = 9x^2 - 8x$.

From $x = -1$ to $x = 0$, y is increasing, hence dy/dx is positive.

Exactly at $x = 0$ the curve is at a maximum point, i.e. y is neither increasing nor decreasing, dy/dx is therefore zero.

Thereafter dy/dx goes negative until the slope is again zero, now at a minimum point so here dy/dx is zero. After this point

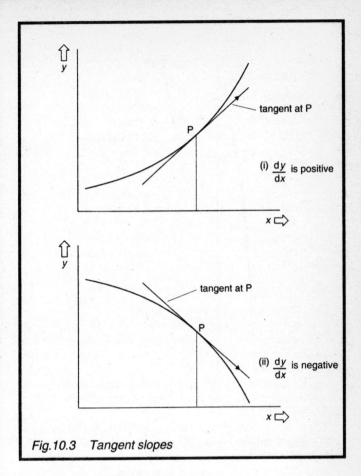

Fig.10.3   Tangent slopes

it is clear that dy/dx becomes positive once more.

Calculation of the maximum and minimum points is therefore straightforward for in each case, as above, dy/dx becomes zero.

We see that when $x = 0$, dy/dx ($= 9x^2 - 8x$) is also equal to 0. Substituting for $x = 0$ in the original equation gives $y = 5$. After this a minimum point is reached when $9x^2 - 8x$ again is equal to 0, i.e. $9x = 8$ and $x = 0.889$. Then $y = 3.946$ as shown in the Figure. There will be no more maxima or minima as the Figure

191

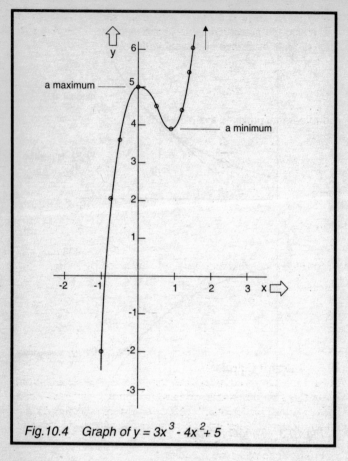

a maximum

a minimum

Fig.10.4   Graph of $y = 3x^3 - 4x^2 + 5$

shows.

Here is a simple exercise which demonstrates the use of differential calculus. Suppose a voltage V is required to drive an electrical machine in series with a controlling resistance R. If a current i flows through the combination of resistance and machine, what value of current is required for maximum power in the machine and what is the power?

Here evidently we need to calculate the rate of change of current with power consumed. The total power provided by the supply is Vi. There is a power loss in the series resistance of i^2R, hence the power available to the machine, $P = Vi - i^2R$. Then the rate of change of current with power:

$$\frac{di}{dP} = V - 2iR$$

and maximum power is available when

$$\frac{di}{dP} = 0,$$

hence $\qquad V - 2iR = 0$

from which $\qquad i = \dfrac{V}{2R}$

Accordingly the maximum value of P is given by

$$i^2R = \frac{V^2}{4R^2} \times R = \frac{V^2}{4R}.$$

10.2 Integral Calculus

Integration can be considered as the inverse of differentiation. What this signifies is that we have to find the function which has a known differential coefficient. More specifically by integration such questions are answered as what is the value of y if for example, $dy/dx = 3x^2$?

From Section 10.1 we found that

$$\frac{d}{dx}(x^3) = 3x^2,$$

hence from this $y = x^3$, so this is one answer which might be set out as follows:

$$y = x^3, \qquad \therefore \frac{dy}{dx} = 3x^2$$

which may be written as $dy = 3x^2 dx$.

Now we introduce the symbol for integration which is $\int$ and so integrating:

$$\int dy = \int 3x^2 dx$$

from which, as shown above, $y = x^3$.

So here is the first rule for integration:

"To find the integral of a power of x, add 1 to the index and divide by the increased index".

It is not quite as straightforward as this however because for example:

$$\frac{d}{dx}(x^3 + 5) = 3x^2 \qquad \frac{d}{dx}(x^3 - 4) = 3x^2$$

On differentiation therefore the constants 5 and -4 have disappeared and so we account for this on integration by adding an arbitrary constant, c, representing any value we choose, hence correctly:

$$y = x^3 + c, \quad \frac{dy}{dx} = 3x^2 \quad \text{and} \quad \int 3x^2 dx = x^3 + c$$

All very complicated so far and we are beginning to realize that in a way the process of integration depends on our recall of the results of differentiation. Let us next find the value of y when $dy/dx = x^2$:

since $\quad \dfrac{d}{dx}(x^3) = 3x^2, \quad$ then $\quad \dfrac{d}{dx}(x^3/3) = 1/3 \times 3x^2 = x^2$

and now introducing the constant c:

$$\frac{d}{dx}(x^3/3 + c) = x^2, \quad \text{hence} \quad y = 1/3x^3 + c.$$

which agrees with the rule for integration above.

194

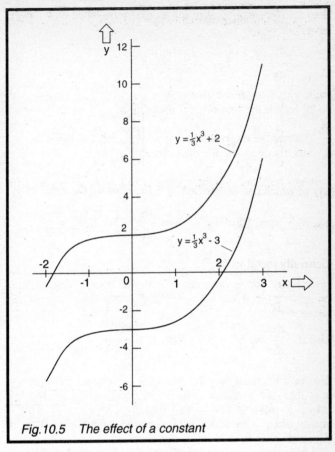

Fig.10.5   The effect of a constant

We have now made a start with integration but let us be more sure of the constant c. On the graphs of for example $y = 1/3x^3 + 2$ and $y = 1/3x^3 - 3$ shown in Figure 10.5, it is clear that at any value of x the tangents to the curves will be the same (hard to believe from the Figure perhaps but the two curves do run parallel). It is the tangent or rate of change of the curves in which we are interested, not on the position of the curve relative to the y axis, hence the actual value of c is immaterial. Here the tangents have the same gradient, i.e. x^2.

195

Here are some examples of the integral form based on what we have done so far:

$$\frac{dy}{dx} \qquad\qquad y$$

$$1 \qquad\qquad x + c$$
$$x \qquad\qquad 1/2x^2 + c$$
$$x^2 \qquad\qquad 1/3x^3 + c$$
$$x^3 \qquad\qquad 1/4x^4 + c$$
$$x^4 \qquad\qquad 1/5x^5 + c$$

any of which can be verified by differentiating the value of y,

e.g. if $\quad y = 1/5x^5 + c \quad$ then $\dfrac{dy}{dx} = 5 \times 1/5x^4 = x^4$

Generally therefore if

$$\frac{dy}{dx} = x^n, \qquad \text{then } y = \frac{x^{n+1}}{n+1} + c$$

also if $\quad \dfrac{dy}{dx} = ax^n \qquad \text{then } y = \dfrac{ax^{n+1}}{n+1} + c$

However we must be wary when $n = -1$ because a function of x is then not available. This is an exceptional case but one which is solvable and in fact then $y = \log_e x + c$. This is mentioned as a reminder that integration is not always straightforward so we have to be on our guard.

Let us now apply the principles so far developed to show the overall process:

function $\rightarrow$ differential coefficient $\rightarrow$ integral $\rightarrow$ function

$$ax^3 \qquad\qquad 3ax^2 \qquad\qquad (3ax^3)/3 + c = ax^3 + c$$

Example – to find y when $dy/dx = 9\sqrt{x}$:

$$dy/dx = 9x^{1/2}$$

so putting a = 9 and n = 1/2, we get :

$$y = \frac{9x^{(1/2+1)} + c}{1/2 + 1} = \frac{9x^{1.5} + c}{1.5} = 6x^{1.5} + c$$

Next – to find y when $dy/dx = 6/x^3$

$$\frac{dy}{dx} = 6.x^{-3}$$

here a = 6, n = −3.

$$\therefore \quad y = \frac{6x^{-3+1}}{-3+1} + c = \frac{6x^{-2}}{-2} + c = \frac{-3}{x^2} + c$$

When dy/dx is the sum of two or more terms, the value of y is obtained by treating each term separately and finally adding the results, e.g.:

find y when $\quad \dfrac{dy}{dx} = 5x^2 - 4 \qquad y = \dfrac{5x^3}{3} - 4x$

Here is a more practical example:

It is given that the acceleration of a certain vehicle is expressed by $0.9 + 0.12t$ metres/sec^2 after a time of t seconds. The initial velocity at $t = 0$ is 2 metres/sec. What is the velocity after 30 seconds?

Let the velocity at t seconds be v m/s. The acceleration is therefore given by the rate of change of velocity with time, i.e. dv/dt m/s^2, here $dv/dt = 0.9 + 0.12t$.

Hence on integration

$$v = 0.9t + 0.12 \times \frac{t^2}{2} + c = 0.9t + 0.06t^2 + c$$

but $v = 2$ when $t = 0$, hence $2 = 0 + 0 + c$, i.e. $c = 2$ and $v = 0.9t + 0.06t^2 + 2$.

After 30 seconds (i.e. $t = 30$), $v = 27 + 54 + 2 = 83$ metres per second.

10.2.1 Integration in Practice

There are many practical uses for integration, here we can do no more than give a broad hint as to its usefulness. Firstly however we need to expand on the way in which the mathematics are written. The symbol $\int$ has already been introduced in Section 10.2, meaning "sum" or "the integral of". We may also need to state the limits between which we are working.

$\int y \, dx$, briefly spoken of as "the integral of $y \, dx$" is used to indicate a function, the differential coefficient of which with respect to x is y. For certain applications such as calculation of distances, areas, volumes, etc., it is necessary to indicate also the limits of the investigation. This is most easily demonstrated by means of an example.

Suppose a body moves in a straight line, travelling a distance s in a time t at a velocity v so that v is known in terms of t. A velocity/time graph is shown in Figure 10.6. However suppose that our interest lies only between the times t_1 and t_2 as shown.

Then the distance travelled between times t_1 and t_2 = increase in s which is the area under the curve between these limits (distance = average velocity × time), written as:

$$\int_{t_2}^{t_1} v \, dt$$

Now let Figure 10.6 be divided by intervals of time δt, producing ordinates of lengths v_1, v_2..., etc., as shown (ignore the figures shown on the axes). For a constant velocity during each interval, the total distance moved would be :

$$v_1 \delta t + v_2 \delta t + ...$$

as can be seen from the Figure by the area under each dotted line. However as δt is made progressively smaller, this sum approaches the limiting value which represents the distance moved. We have already shown this to be:

$$\int_{t_2}^{t_1} v \, dt$$

198

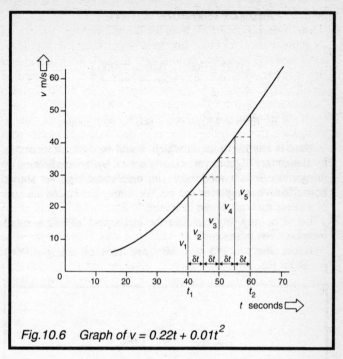

Fig.10.6   Graph of $v = 0.22t + 0.01t^2$

As an example, suppose the motion of a body after t seconds to be expressed by

$$v = 0.22t + 0.01t^2 \text{ metres per second.}$$

How far does the body travel between 30 and 60 seconds? (Figure 10.6 shows this particular curve.)

Distance travelled

$$\int_{30}^{60} v\,dt = \int_{30}^{60} (0.22t + 0.01t^2)\,dt = \left[\frac{0.22t^2}{2} + \frac{0.01t^3}{3}\right]_{30}^{60}$$

$$= \left[\frac{0.22 \times 3600}{2} + \frac{0.01 \times 216000}{3} \right] -$$

$$- \left[\frac{0.22 \times 900}{2} + \frac{0.01 \times 27000}{3} \right]$$

$$= (396 + 720) - (99 + 90) = 927 \text{ metres.}$$

Here is another formula which would be difficult to obtain by elementary algebra yet is easily solved by the application of integration. It is a moderately uncomplicated one yet shows how effective integration can be. We simply determine the area of a circle such as shown in Figure 10.7.

Let θ be any angle within the circle and $\angle POQ$ a small increase, $(\delta\theta)$ in the angle.

Hence the arc $PQ = r\,\delta\theta$ and area of triangle $POQ = \frac{1}{2}PQ \times OS$.

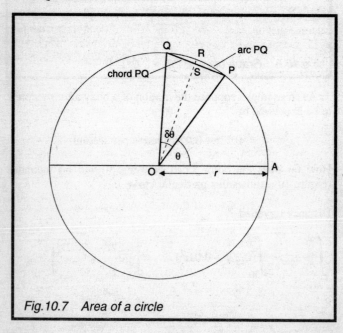

Fig. 10.7   Area of a circle

When ∠POQ becomes indefinitely small the arc PRQ becomes equal to the chord PSQ, i.e. S and R join, then:

$$\text{area of triangle POQ} = \tfrac{1}{2}r\delta\theta \times r = \tfrac{1}{2}r^2\delta\theta$$

The sum of all such triangles varying from 0 to 2π (radians) gives the area of the circle, i.e.:

$$\text{area of circle} = \int_0^{2\pi} \tfrac{1}{2}r^2 d\theta = \int_0^{2\pi} r^2/2 \, d\theta$$

(we can take $r^2/2$ out from the integral sign because it remains constant)

$$\therefore \quad \text{area} = \frac{r^2}{2}\left[\theta\right]_0^{2\pi} = \left[\frac{r^2}{2} \times 2\pi\right] - \left[\frac{r^2}{2} \times 0\right] = \pi r^2$$

This is perhaps as far as we should venture into the realms of calculus, having now done sufficient for a good understanding of its purpose and capabilities. Undoubtedly when many types of change are involved, differential and integral calculus are there to help us.

Chapter 11

ELECTRONIC SWITCHING

We have examined the general principles of binary notation in Section 1.3 and a Table for help in binary/decimal conversion is given in Appendix 5. In this Chapter we go one stage further in considering how electronic digital systems are designed. The basic mathematics for such design is known as *Boolean Algebra*. This is attributed to George Boole (an English mathematician) who in 1854 decided that some logical thought, usually considered to be a human attribute only, could actually be expressed by a special algebra. His work is now readily applied to the design of digital systems. By this, parts of a circuit are represented by groups of symbols and from the relationships between the symbols the operation of the complete circuit is determined. The basic symbols used are 1 for *true* and 0 for *false*. We may find the terms *logic 1* and *logic 0* in use but generally the simple 1 and 0 are sufficient. Logical reasoning is the essence of computer activity hence their use of Boolean algebra. The algebra is in fact used in the design of most digital switching systems, usually with the aim of reducing circuitry and components to a minimum.

11.1 The Basic Logical Relationships
The three main propositions used in Boolean algebra are labelled AND, OR and NOT (note the capitals). These labels in fact indicate how various digital *gates* function. A gate is an electrical circuit with a single output which depends on one or more input signals together. It is in fact a digital switch which only operates to a predetermined input arrangement. Modern integrated circuit packages may contain thousands, even hundreds of thousands of such gates. Here we look at these three types of gate only, there are several others, each with its own special facilities.

11.1.1 AND and OR Gates
Logic is the science of reasoning and we use logic in answering the question as to how X can be connected electrically to Y in

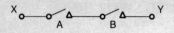

(i) when A and B close,
X is connected to Y

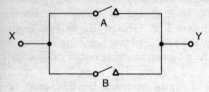

(ii) when either A or B close,
X is connected to Y

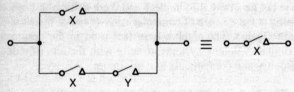

(iii) a logic theorem - 3 switches reduced to 1

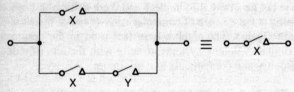

(iv) 4 switches reduced to 3

Fig.11.1   Logic theorems

the AND and OR gates shown in Figure 11.1(i) and (ii). The difference between the two gates is immediately evident for logic tells that in (i) X reaches Y electrically only when both A AND B are closed, yet in (ii) X reaches Y when either A OR B is closed. If we imagine that an open contact represents a logic 0 and a closed contact a 1, then *truth tables* can be drawn up for the two gates. A truth table is a list indicating the truth or falsity (1 or 0) of each operation. f represents the gate operation, i.e. X through to Y.

AND Gate				OR Gate		
A	B	f		A	B	f
0	0	0		0	0	0
1	0	0		1	0	1
0	1	0		0	1	1
1	1	1		1	1	1

Of course these are simple gates, usually designed around one or two transistors working at 5 V. Designers have to battle with considerably more complicated ones.

11.1.2 The NOT Gate
This gate simply reverses the input signal at its output, hence if presented with a 0 the output is 1 and vice versa. It is frequently used with other gates to change over an input condition or equally to change over an output condition.

11.1.3 Logic Theorems
There are many theorems available for designers, mostly used with the objective of reducing the number of gates required for a particular purpose. Two only are shown in Figure 11.1(iii) and (iv). In (iii) the two parallel paths are X OR (X AND Y) and it is clear that operation of a single X contact is all that is needed to switch the circuit through. (iv) in the Figure is a little more complex, the two parallel paths are (X AND Y) and (X AND Z). On the right hand side of the drawing it is shown that the same facilities are obtained with a single X contact in series with Y and Z in parallel i.e. X AND (Y OR Z).

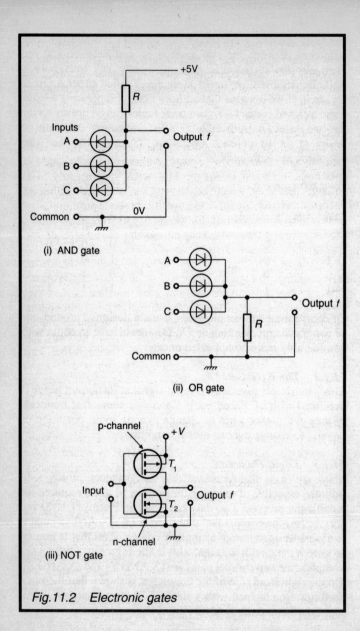

Fig.11.2 Electronic gates

These results are of course obvious and are the simplest of logic theorems, there are many much more complicated and in fact most switching requirements are not so easily resolved but can be met by use of one of the theorems or a combination of several.

11.1.4 Logic Gate Circuits

We can no more than demonstrate the basic ideas involved in the design of electronic logic gates. Although the AND and OR gate circuits shown in Figure 11.2 work satisfactorily, it is unlikely that they would be chosen for inclusion within an integrated circuit, mainly because the power consumption is relatively high. In contrast, for the NOT gate the circuit chosen employs special types of transistors suitable for integration and having very low current requirements.

A 3-input AND gate circuit employing *diode-resistance logic* is shown in Figure 11.2(i). If a digital 0 is received on any input terminal, its diode becomes of low resistance, current then flows through R and via that input terminal to the common line. The current through R creates a voltage drop so that the output terminal f is almost at 0 V potential. Put in another way, f is shunted by a low (diode) resistance to the common line. This condition is reinforced if more than one input is at logic 0. When and only when all inputs are at logic 1 (+5 V) do the diodes reach a high-resistance state for then the potentials on both sides are equal, hence no current flows. f is then at logic 1 because it is almost at the potential of the 5 V supply line.

The OR gate shown in (ii) also uses diode-resistance logic. It requires no power supply because this is provided by the input signal (usually this is a disadvantage). Hence with logic 0 at the input terminals, the output f must be at 0 because there is no voltage anywhere. When any input goes positive to logic 1, that particular diode conducts and provides a through path for the potential to reach f.

The NOT gate circuit shown in (iii) looks more complicated than it is. Two complementary metal-oxide semiconductor transistors (CMOS – a special type which has especially low current requirements and is used in integrated circuits) are employed, one n-channel, the other p-channel. When the input is around 0 V, T_1 conducts hence the output terminal voltage rises towards that of the positive line. Conversely when the input is at 5 V, T_2 conducts and the output terminal voltage falls, the output is therefore an inversion of the input.

* * * * *

This is where we must stop for fear of getting out of our depth!

Appendix 1

MATHEMATICAL SIGNS AND SYMBOLS

Sign or Symbol

$=$	is equal to
$\equiv$	is equivalent to
$\approx$	is approximately equal to
$\neq$	is not equal to
$\therefore$	therefore
$\rightarrow$	tends to or approaches
$>$	is greater than
$<$	is less than
$\sqrt{}$	square root of
$\sqrt[n]{}$	nth root of
$\angle$	angle
$\propto$	varies as
$\sum$	sum
$\prod$	product
f	function, f
$f(x)$	value of the function f at x
j	$\sqrt{-1}$
π	ratio of circumference to diameter of circle ($\approx 3.141\ 592\ 654$)
e	base of natural logarithms ($\approx 2.718\ 281\ 828$)
e^x, exp x	exponential function of x
$\log_a x$	logarithm to the base a of x.

Appendix 2

THE INTERNATIONAL SYSTEM OF UNITS (SI)

Prior to international agreement on the SI system in 1960, many countries had their own systems of units although the metric which has the advantage of simplicity in using a single multiple only (10) predominated. One advantage of the SI system is that it is a fully *coherent* (joining together) system. A system of units is said to be coherent if the product or quotient of any two unit quantities is the unit of the resultant quantity. The SI is also described as a *rational* system, which is one which is expressible as a ratio of whole numbers.

A coherent unit system must therefore have as its basis a group of independent base units which must be defined unambiguously. The SI has 7 such units with two supplementary ones:

Quantity	Unit Name	Unit Symbol
length	metre	m
mass	kilogram	kg
time	second	s
current	ampere	A
temperature	kelvin	K
luminous intensity	candela	cd
amount of substance	mole	mol

Supplementary units:

Plane angle	radian	rad
Solid angle	steradian	sr

A2.1 Derived Units
The units given below are derived from those above and have been given names as shown:

210

Quantity	Unit name	SI Units	Unit Symbol
Force	newton	kg m/s^2	N
Energy	joule	N m	J
Power	watt	J/s	W
Pressure, stress	pascal	N/m^2	Pa
Electric potential	volt	J/C, W/A	V
Electric charge, electric flux	coulomb	A s	C
Magnetic flux	weber	V s	Wb
Magnetic flux density	tesla	Wb/m^2	T
Resistance	ohm	V/A	Ω
Conductance	siemens	A/V	S
Capacitance	farad	C/V	F
Inductance	henry	Wb/A	H
Celsius temperature	degree celsius	K	°C
Frequency	hertz	s^{-1}	Hz

Appendix 3

MULTIPLES AND SUB-MULTIPLES OF UNITS

A significant advantage of the metric system is that, whatever the unit, for example a length of one metre or weight of one gram, larger or smaller quantities are all described by the same range of prefixes. Some of the multiples and/or sub-multiples will be found to occur more frequently than others depending mainly on the convenience of the size of the unit and how usage has grown traditionally. As an example, one gram is such a small weight for shopping that a kilogram (1000 grams) is more likely to be used. The same holds good in electronics, for example, a capacitance of one farad is so large that the micro-farad, nanofarad and picofarad are more likely to be found in everyday use (see also Appendix 2).

Multiplication factor	Prefix	Symbol
10^{18}	exa	E
10^{15}	peta	P
10^{12}	tera	T
10^{9}	giga	G
10^{6}	mega	M
10^{3}	kilo	k
10^{2}	hecto	h
10^{1}	deca	da
10^{-1}	deci	d
10^{-2}	centi	c
10^{-3}	milli	m
10^{-6}	micro	μ
10^{-9}	nano	n
10^{-12}	pico	p
10^{-15}	femto	f
10^{-18}	atto	a

Examples are:

1 GHz is the symbol used to simplify 1 000 000 000 (one thousand million) hertz (10^9 Hz).

1 kilometre (1 km) is used in preference to 1 000 metres.

1 nanofarad (1 nF) is used in preference to 10^{-9} farads (one thousand millionth of one farad).

Appendix 4

TABLE OF POWERS OF 2

n	2^n	n	2^n
0	1	12	4096
1	2	13	8192
2	4	14	16 384
3	8	15	32 768
4	16	16	65 536
5	32		
6	64	-1	0.5
7	128	-2	0.25
8	256	-3	0.125
9	512	-4	0.0625
10	1024	-5	0.031 25
11	2048	-6	0.015 625

Appendix 5

BINARY/DECIMAL CONVERSION

In Section 1.3.1 is discussed briefly the use of 8-bit (one byte) binary codes. There are 256 different combinations of 0's and 1's obtainable from such a code. This Appendix shows them all in a 16 × 16 Table with their decimal equivalents. The latter are in fact not 1–256 but 0–255. Although the Table itself is more or less self-explanatory, here are two examples :

Conversion of decimal 219 to binary:
Decimal 219 is found in the third column from the right and fifth line up. The first four bits of the binary equivalent are at the head of the column, i.e. 1101. The second four bits are in the column at the extreme left, fifth from the bottom, i.e. 1011. The full binary number is therefore 11011011.

Conversion of binary 00100001 to decimal:
The first four bits are 0010 and therefore the required number is in the third column. The second four bits are 0001 and appear in the second line down of the left-hand column. At third column, second line down is the equivalent decimal number, i.e. 33.

1st 4 → bits / 2nd 4 ↓ bits	0000	0001	0010	0011	0100	0101	0110	0111	1000	1001	1010	1011	1100	1101	1110	1111
0000	0	16	32	48	64	80	96	112	128	144	160	176	192	208	224	240
0001	1	17	33	49	65	81	97	113	129	145	161	177	193	209	225	241
0010	2	18	34	50	66	82	98	114	130	146	162	178	194	210	226	242
0011	3	19	35	51	67	83	99	115	131	147	163	179	195	211	227	243
0100	4	20	36	52	68	84	100	116	132	148	164	180	196	212	228	244
0101	5	21	37	53	69	85	101	117	133	149	165	181	197	213	229	245
0110	6	22	38	54	70	86	102	118	134	150	166	182	198	214	230	246
0111	7	23	39	55	71	87	103	119	135	151	167	183	199	215	231	247
1000	8	24	40	56	72	88	104	120	136	152	168	184	200	216	232	248
1001	9	25	41	57	73	89	105	121	137	153	169	185	201	217	233	249
1010	10	26	42	58	74	90	106	122	138	154	170	186	202	218	234	250
1011	11	27	43	59	75	91	107	123	139	155	171	187	203	219	235	251
1100	12	28	44	60	76	92	108	124	140	156	172	188	204	220	236	252
1101	13	29	45	61	77	93	109	125	141	157	173	189	205	221	237	253
1110	14	30	46	62	78	94	110	126	142	158	174	190	206	222	238	254
1111	15	31	47	63	79	95	111	127	143	159	175	191	207	223	239	255